MW00614771

A Gathering of Heroes

STATE SENATOR GENE STIPE'S

A GATHERING OF HEROES

by Ralph Marsh
in collaboration with Gene Stipe

Spring
Mountain

A Gathering of Heroes

Printed in the United States of America

First Printing

ISBN 0-9704309-0-6

Library of Congress Catalog Number 00-108608

Designed and produced by 2W Design Group; Oklahoma City, Oklahoma
Illustrated by Corey Wolfe; Battle Ground, Washington

 Spring Mountain

HC 64 Box 4650, Heavener, Oklahoma 74937

CONTENTS

— *p a r t   f o u r* —

ACKNOWLEDGMENTS

Ed Montgomery is one of the more delightful people I have met in a half-century of being associated with writing in one way or another. In those five decades, the only person at whom I have ever heard Ed swear was himself, and then only once, and gently. So it was natural that, when I wanted a writer's reality check – straightforward but gentle – that I would turn to him. He was the first reader of the manuscript of Heroes. And he was straightforward. And gentle.

Also, thanks to Gini Moore Campbell at Oklahoma Heritage Association for her assistance with the manuscript.

The directly quoted text in "Vietnamization" is from *Blues Bastards*, by Randall Herrod, Regnery Gateway Press.

Other publications most helpful in fleshing out the narrative of *Heroes* were *Chronicles of Oklahoma*, Oklahoma Historical Society; *Then to the Rock Let Me Fly*, by Jace Weaver, University of Oklahoma Press; *Route 66: The Mother Road*, by Michael Wallis, St. Martin's Press; *The Story of Oklahoma*, W. David Baird & Danney Goble, University of Oklahoma Press; *Moments in Oklahoma History*, By Bonnie Speer, Reliance Press; *Guideposts Magazine*, and *Journal*, Oklahoma State Medical Association.

PROLOGUE

February, 1997. Eighteen degrees and snowing. The '94 bronze Cadillac pitched over the steep peak of a freshly gouged oil-field road, and its driver studied his passenger out of the corner of his eye while the big car thumped its way through a downhill slide toward a drilling rig on the shore of Lake Eufaula. And I cannot remember whether the story was of Lloyd Rader slickering the federal government out of millions in seed money for the Oklahoma Health Sciences Center or the role brown eggs played in the building of the McAlester Turnpike, but it was, by nature of the story-teller, a quick, personal visit to one of the little-known but significant moments in how the State of Oklahoma came to be what it is today.

Oklahoma was only 41 years old when the storyteller first was elected to the Oklahoma Legislature. More than a half-century ago, in the year 1948, when he was a young student of the law still turning 21. The year Harry Truman was elected to his full term as President, Robert S. Kerr was elected to the United States Senate, Gandhi died and the State of Israel was born. All the young veterans who survived World War II came storming home and into college classrooms and public office, becoming Oklahoma's second generation of frontiersmen, announcing to the world that a new kind of stampede was on in Oklahoma, and this one was not for land. But for new ideas. Different ways of doing things. And, in the years since, the storyteller had become the longest-serving elected public official in the world, involved in some way in just about everything of significance that had happened politically in Oklahoma during that half-century. And all those classic little stories were tucked handily just inside his mind.

On this particular Saturday afternoon, State Senator Gene Stipe was in a good mood despite the cold and drizzle. It was barely past noon, and already it had been a good day. About 40 people had come through his office, some wanting work, a couple wanting to file a class-action lawsuit, a woman whose son was in his first trouble with the law, and a little schizophrenic fellow who dropped by just to hear the senator tell him again that he really did amount to something in the scheme of things. And Gene had finished it all in time to get to Poppa J's on Highway 9 for an outstanding sandwich of barbecued beef and a short catch-up on the OU game before heading off for an afternoon of roaming the backroads of Pittsburg County. Telling Oklahoma stories.

During the last half of the 20th century, Gene Stipe has collected stories the way some people collect pocket knives or books or statuettes of angels. Common folk. Famous folk. Notorious folk. The fascination, he says, is that everybody has his own entirely individual characteristics. The one person as important in his own way as the other.

Stipe stories have to be hand-gleaned painstakingly from in between and twisted around the sounds of the bronze Cadillac's tires beating their rapid rhythm on the highway or sluffing their way slowly through river gravel on a rock shelf of a southeastern Oklahoma hill. Snatched quickly from between notes of Italian music in a fine restaurant in Krebs, extracted from the wet slap and sizzle of onions and hamburger at Ray's grill in McAlester, because Gene Stipe interviews that last longer than five minutes are on the move. There are few things Gene Stipe will accept that he cannot do. But sitting around is one.

"Never did learn how to do that."

And so, we started what may be the world's longest-running (in highway mileage, at least) interview, done in the '94 bronze Cadillac in installments tucked around a morning meeting in McAlester, a court case in Muskogee, and a telephone rate hearing in Oklahoma City, getting back to McAlester before his law office staff could sneak off home at the proper quitting time. I had some idea the stories in the growing pile were going somewhere, but I couldn't figure out where. And then, without warning – in Hartshorne, maybe, or looking at a litter of Dalmatian pups out by Eufaula – it happened.

"The people of my generation," he said, "were blessed to live in difficult times – from the Great Depression to the Millennium, those of us who were lucky – probably the most meaningful times in the history of this country. And those times produced some heroes. Bona fide heroes. Most folks don't even know who those old boys were. I've always wanted the people of Oklahoma to know them the way I did. I've said for years that somebody sure ought to write a book about those fellows, but nobody ever would.

"So I guess you and I had better get about it."

And we did.

This is a book of fact. But it is a book of fact as remembered by people who lived it many, many years ago. Where possible, memories have been checked against standard accounts of the same events and – when there was a variation – a choice was made which way to go, always cleaving to the most likely, the most interesting, the most human.

We hope you like it.

—Ralph Marsh

part one

The smell of outdoor fires covered
the mountain. Screams of terrified
hogs echoed in the hollows. Steam
rose from big iron kettles of water.
The spat of .22 rifles and the
profuse flowing of blood from the
throats of stuck hogs were anything but frightening sounds to a
kid on Peaceable Mountain. They
meant pork chops on the table.
There was something mighty
encouraging about storing up all
that meat although you knew
from the past that it would be
gone before winter was.

1933

"My friends…" Warm and reassuring as a woodfire on a cold evening. "We are not going through another winter like the last."

The words eased into the souls of frightened people gathered in their homes or listening beneath the opened windows of neighbors prosperous enough to own a radio. Franklin Delano Roosevelt – beginning his 12 years as President of the United States – was talking with his folks "…in the big industries, in the little shops, in the great cities and in the small villages…"

A third of the American work force was without jobs, and those who were working drew half pay. A farmer had to plant, fertilize, raise, harvest and sell nine bushels of wheat to replace the shoes he wore out producing it.

"All we have to fear," Roosevelt said, "is fear itself."

From the other side of the world a different voice came. Adolf Hitler was beginning his 12 years in power. Hatred spewed from his microphone and seeped across Germany and leaked out, infecting the whole world.

1

When All You Own Hangs in Balance

The sudden onset of the elm switch stung the boy like swarming yellowjackets. Milk splattered the boards of the kitchen floor amid the clanging of the dropped buckets.

"Mama! Why you whuppin' on me?"

"I told ... you and told ... you and told ... you to start that ... fire first ... thing you get ... up. I get ... up here to ... fix breakfast ... that stove ... colder 'n' the ice box."

The boy fled out the back screen door and behind the barn, the stinging in his arms and shoulders seeping into his insides. He had started the fire. Just as he had done every morning of his life that he could remember. No way for him to know it went out while he was feeding the mules and milking the cows.

"Wade? Wade! You git out of behind that barn and hitch that mule!"

It had been more to the boy than a switching. Every time the elm slip had landed, it had hit a spot already sore. From following a mule's tail through corn higher than his head when it was so hot the corn leaves crackled and cut at his ears. From being too big to be a kid and too young to be a man on a farm in McIntosh County, Oklahoma, in a year when nobody or even everybody together was big enough or strong enough to work hard enough or long enough to get enough food for the table.

Sore from standing beside his little brother, Buddy, in the drug store in Eufaula waiting for the white man to get Mama's prescription, yearning with all of a young soul for a lick of the ice cream starting to melt and run in precious, sticky drops down over buff-brown cones and cradling black fists. The hard watching eyes of the white man.

"Don't you eat that in here, boy. Negroes eat outside."

"Wade?"

"I didn't lick it, Mama. I ain't going to."

And now, a switchin'. First thing in the morning without even asking if he had started the fire.

To a Negro boy on a McIntosh County farm in the year 1933, Oklahoma bore little resemblance to what it had been promised to be in the beginning. First word of Oklahoma! had thrilled a younger, happier world, promising whatever the listener wished to hear. An all-Indian state free of white land grabbers, an all-Negro state free of red-neck crackers, an all-white state free of Negroes. Equality. Free thought. Free land never plowed. All to be had in Oklahoma! It had screamed from land promoters' pamphlets, clicked through telegraph wires and passed by word of mouth from farm to farm and tavern to tavern. But, after a half-century, the legendary six-guns and thundering hooves had fallen quiet. The heroes had gone.

The Choctaw, Chickasaw, Cherokee, Creek and Seminole Indians had made their way to Oklahoma through cold, sick-walking miles from their homes in Georgia and Alabama and Mississippi, Tennessee, and the Carolinas, kept up and moving by the hope of fresh, new all-Indian-forever country. Tribes and clans were broken now, disbanded, full-bloods hiding in the southeastern Oklahoma mountains where they lived even poorer but freer than their town kin.

Negroes had streamed onto the land by the tens of thousands with scars of slavery fresh on their backs and bright new dreams pressed into their minds by the promoters' pamphlets with which they had long since patched cracks in their cabins.

The proud whites, even. Ground for which they had sacrificed so much of other people and themselves had been cottoned down to a dull grey-reddish soil that blew in the wind with their dreams, piling up against the pitiful little fortresses they had erected.

Out in the western part of the state, dust storms and bankers were driving Oklahoma dirt farmers in herds from their only means of living. Word got around, somehow, to go to Custer County where there was a young man with access to relief checks he was eager to hand out. So many people began receiving their tiny emergency relief checks in Custer County the administration of Republican President Herbert Hoover sent an investigator out to see if there was fraud. He discovered a tent city on the Washita River near Clinton filled with dirt farmers who hadn't money enough to live where they were or to flee to where they could make a living. Their little checks were being delivered to them by an unknown young man Governor Alfalfa Bill Murray had named administrator of relief for Custer County. The federal investigator walked through the tent city and talked with the starving farmers, got on the train and went back to Washington. No fraud, he told his bosses, just some young guy who had figured out a perfectly legal scheme to get some relief for his folks.

"What was that kid's name?"

"Rader, I believe it was. Lloyd Edwin Rader."

"Wade!"

The boy carefully skirted the reach of his Mama and went to the rope line on which the drying clothes hung. Pulled his best shirt off it and the pair of pants with the fewest patches. Rolled them into a bundle and tucked them under his arm.

"Wade?"

"Mama, I ain't hitchin' that mule this mornin'."

"Jus' what you gon do?"

"I'm a leavin', Mama."

"What you gon eat, boy? Where you gon stay?"

"Going where they ain't gon be no switchin', Mama."

"You get back here, Wade!"

"No, Mama, I'm a leavin'."

The woman's fury wilted.

"Come here, son. For jes one minute."

The boy shuffled cautiously back into the yard, keeping his eyes on his mama's hands. She reached deep into a seldom-seen pocket and pulled out a handkerchief, untied its four corners and dropped its contents into the boy's hand. He stared. A dollar, two quarters and a nickel! A week of Mama's washing work. Two days scrubbing on the rub board, two days ironing with the heavy old iron heated on the stove. White folks' clothes. White folks' money. Miz Watts turned quickly back into the house. The boy wrapped the two quarters and the nickel into the dollar bill and tucked it deep into his pocket. And walked out through the gate and into the road. The money his mama had dropped into his hand had taken some of the sting from his arms and shoulders, but had not eased the smarting inside.

"Mr. Bob, I want to borrow a little money this morning."

"Watts? How much money you want?"

The boy wagged his head in a shamed kind of derision. It was a ritual of spring for his daddy, Charlie Watts.

"Well, Mr. Bob, it'll take about $150 to make this crop."

Charlie Watts, small and neat and compact and white-looking enough to pass – a man who once raised 13,000 bushels of wheat in a single year in Canada – would pick out a particular day in spring, special as the first day for planting corn, and he would call his son and they would walk together down to the bank in Eufaula. And Charlie Watts would walk straight and tall for a man who was smaller than his wife. Then, Charlie Watts would stop outside the bank and remove his hat, and he and his boy would go in.

"Hundred and fifty dollars! By God, Watts, that's a hell of a lot of money. By God, I don't know. I don't know about that, Watts."

Old white Mr. Bob would pace the floor for a long time.

"Watts, you still got them two teams of mules?"

"Yessir."

Mr. Bob would write it down on a sheet of paper.

"How many head of cattle you got, Watts?"

"I got 25."

And the cattle went onto the sheet of paper.

"How many head of hogs you got?"

"I got 12 head of hogs."

"How many chickens you got?"

"Well, I got about 60 head of chickens."

"You still got them two wagons?"

"Yessir, still got 'em."

And before it was over, everything the family owned, including the house and the ice box, was written down on that sheet of paper. And it would hang there in scary balance until fall when the crops came in and everything was counted up. Come fall and not enough crop to pay that $150, old Mr. Bob would clean Charlie out. Move him out of his house and put him and his family to going down that dusty, rose-colored road. It had been that way for as long as the boy could remember.

McIntosh County sits dead center in the eastern half of Oklahoma, the half that remained Indian Territory until it joined the white man's Oklahoma Territory and became a state in 1907. The county is named for a prominent Creek Indian family whose culture and traditions equaled or exceeded those of the whites.

Eufaula sits at the southern edge of McIntosh County. It is named for an old Indian town on the west bank of the Chattahoochee River in Alabama where the Creeks lived before they were herded west by the whites. The word Eufaula in the Creek Indian language means "they split up here and went other places."

2

Freedom-Walking Shoes

William Henry David Murray, day laborer, farmer, teacher, salesman, self-taught lawyer, firm believer in alfalfa pasturage and purity of bloodlines had as much as anybody to do with the kind of state in which the Negro boy Wade found himself living in 1933. Murray was a Texan, a tall man with big ears and mustache and an ego of heroic proportions. He came to the Indian Country in 1898, convinced himself that the Chickasaws were an Aryan people and married the niece of the tribal governor, thus becoming an immediately prominent member of that nation of Indians, which owned all the land thereabout. He helped the Indians to write a constitution to set up an all-Indian state named Sequoyah, of which he would have been an automatic citizen by marriage. When that failed, he became president of the constitutional convention that made Oklahoma into a white man's state of which he was an automatic citizen by blood.

Murray loved the family farm and feared big government and big corporations as the religious fear the devil. When his obsessions were meshed with those of new-country farmers and laboring men and reform-minded women of Oklahoma and Indian territories, the resulting constitution was so progressive and forward-looking and protective of human rights that the proposed new State of Oklahoma became the talk of the whole world. In Europe, the Oklahoma Constitution was compared to the Magna Carta in the lengths to which it went to assure human freedoms. Murray was so afraid somebody might change a word of the document that he carried it around with him in a tin box – eating his meals, sometimes, with it clutched between his knees.

Murray loved to tell a good story. One of his favorites happened in early spring back in 1908 by which time he was speaker of Oklahoma's first House of Representatives, overseeing the writing of the first set of laws under which the incredible guarantees of freedom would flow from the constitution to the people of the new state. The legislature was meeting in the city hall of Guthrie which the state had contracted as a meeting place until a permanent one could be built. A sergeant at arms came running to tell Speaker Murray that the basement was full of angry citizens of the new State of Oklahoma, and that they were chanting his name. Murray walked down the stairs, listening to them chant "Think of Bill Murray and Then Vote!"

Here is how Murray – self-styled contributing editor of one of the most progressive documents in history – would tell that story in his gravelly voice:

"There was about thirty standing around the city marshal's office. I said, 'What in hell are you niggers doing down here?'

"One of them knew me. He said, 'That's Alfalfa Bill!' And he jumped to get out of there, and every one of them run up the steps and got outside."

Murray always had to stop to laugh when he remembered how those Negroes looked running.

"That sergeant at arms," he would chuckle, "just didn't know how to handle those people."

And he walked back upstairs to resume his work of writing laws to guarantee equal rights to Oklahoma's citizens.

In early Oklahoma Territory days, racial relations were handled at the county level. In one Lincoln County school, Negroes and whites sat in adjoining rooms in an abandoned farmhouse, and the teacher lectured to the separated races simultaneously from the hallway. In 1901, Oklahoma Territory ordered segregation of schools and forbade teaching of one race by members of the other. It provided for separate county school funds for each of the two races.

Everybody knew President Theodore Roosevelt would decline to sign a proposed Oklahoma Constitution with racial discrimination in it. Murray made sure it contained readymade loopholes. It provided separate schools for white and colored children with like accommodations, impartially maintained. Colored children, it said, were children of African descent. Everybody else in this last home of the American Indian was, by legislative pronouncement, white.

When the first legislature of the new state convened in December, 1907, the first bills introduced in both houses required separate coaches and waiting rooms for African-Americans in all railway facilities. Later laws mandated separate telephone booths, cemeteries, and even separate boats when fishing. William Henry David Murray stayed in the Oklahoma Legislature long enough to be sure that laws were written to see that government, big corporations, and Negroes were kept in their places and that universities taught good farming and women knew their places as mothers and housewives and loyal mates to their men. Then he won election to the United States Congress to spread his concept of good living to the nation as a whole. Oklahoma voters turned him out in 1916 and rebuffed his attempt at the governor's mansion in 1918.

Furious, Murray said all those basic values that made Oklahoma so great so quick were disappearing. And so did he.

❖

The Negro boy Wade was far out of sight of the little farmhouse that sat outside Eufaula on the 15 acres the family owned. It was the same road the boy walked two miles to school, stepping to the side for the schoolbus, a sunflower-yellow vehicle with four or five white children scattered among its 25 seats. It would drive right on past the boy's schoolhouse just as it had driven on past the boy. He would sit in his separate school with muscles tensed to keep from sliding down against the boy next to him because the legs of the desks already were broken when they were brought over from the school to which the bus was taking the white children. White children's names already be scrawled on what remained of the covers on the books. Pages torn out. Crayola marks on them. The bus would go right on past where the lone basketball goal hung netless over dirt to where the white kids clamored and laughed in two gymnasiums. Wade kicked a rock from the road, lofted it clear over the straggly barbed wire fence and into a field of corn.

The Negroes hadn't lost every fight. Wade could remember the timbre of Negro teachers' voices changing when they told how black folks had challenged the so-called Grandfather Clause, which in effect allowed only white men to vote. It had surfaced when Republicans won three congressional House seats from Oklahoma, and Democratic leaders blamed black voters. The second state legislature, controlled by Democrats, passed a literacy requirement but didn't set standards for the test, so a red-necked registrar could ask a Negro anything he wanted to. On June 1, 1915, the United States Supreme Court struck down the Grandfather Clause and blacks in Oklahoma kept at least the right to vote for the white men.

Behind the Negro victory was Roscoe Dunjee, founder and editor of *The Black Dispatch*, Oklahoma City's African-American newspaper. Dunjee was the son of John Dunjee, a slave who had escaped through the Underground Railroad and had become a Baptist minister and ended up in Oklahoma Territory. He taught his son, Roscoe, that he was just as good as any white man.

Wade grinned at the thought of Roscoe Dunjee. And, again at the thought of his daddy, Charlie Watts. In some ways they were alike, although Charlie couldn't afford white man's clothes like Roscoe could. Lotta times people thought they were getting the best of Charlie Watts, and then they found out they were not.

Getting happier by the mile, the boy chunked a rock at a white man's dog that ran out to bark at him. Even dirt smells different when it is scuffed up by freedom-walking shoes on a bright, sunshiny day with no corn leaves cutting across your face.

His daddy had actually turned the tables on old white Mr. Bob when President Roosevelt closed the banks and like to have scared everybody to death. Charlie Watts had $19 in that bank, and that was a lot of money. Man could walk to town with a couple of dollars and he couldn't bring back everything on his shoulders that he could buy with that two dollars. Fifty-pound sack of flour for 48 cents. And then Mama would take that flower sack and she would make the boys little shirts and the girls little skirts and blouses. Nineteen dollars was the difference between having something and having nothing at all.

Charlie Watts got up early on the morning after he heard the talk that the banks had closed. He got his hat and called the boy and they walked to Mr. Bob's house and knocked on the back door, and Charlie Watts removed his hat and asked to see Mr. Bob.

"My $19 still in that bank?"

And it was Mr. Bob's turn to fidget under his daddy's eyes as he tried to explain that the President had closed down the bank to protect Charlie's money.

"I'd as soon look after it myself, Mr. Bob."

And they left.

And the next day Charlie Watts got up and got his hat and called his boy and they walked to Mr. Bob's.

"My money still in that bank?"

Finally, Mr. Bob folded.

"Watts, I'm going to give you that little money so I can rest."

Charlie held out his hand and Mr. Bob counted $19 into it from his pocket.

And Charlie Watts clapped his hat back on his head and walked off down that street feeling of his money in the pocket of his overalls while rich white men all over the United States were having to wait for theirs.

The road, Wade knew, would take him southwest for ten miles down into Pittsburg County where the steam engines slowed to a crawl on the grade into the town of Canadian. He had seen beaten men accept the invitation of open boxcar doors there to jump in and be whisked away, their crazily happy eyes locking for a fraction of a second with the big eyes of a Negro boy picking trackside blackberries with his mama.

By the end of the 1920s, William Henry David Murray had been little more than an arrogant memory from the good old days when the state was Oklahoma with an exclamation point. But on those days when the dust blew and the dry corn leaves rattled, Oklahomans got to remembering those early days of fresh dreams and good promises and wishing it could be that way again.

And then the old man came back. He had been in Bolivia, South America, he said, trying to build a farming colony in which Aryan, gentile gentlemen would rule over families of virtuous and obedient wives and children. It had failed there because such ideas, he had come to believe, had trouble thriving in foreign soil. But, he was ready to try it again in Oklahoma. His problem, he said, was that he hadn't known that the number nine was his own special luck number.

So, he changed his name from William Henry David Murray to Wm. H. Murray so it contained nine letters, returned to Oklahoma on August 29, 1929, borrowed $29 from his hometown bank in Tishomingo, and ran again for governor of Oklahoma. Sixty-six years old, now, he would spit tobacco juice on the floor and if a squeamish host moved the spittoon to where he had spit last, he would spit where the spittoon had been before. And it was easy, somehow, for Oklahoma to identify with an old man back from the days of Oklahoma's creation. An old man who had staked everything on his ability to make it big in Oklahoma – as they had – only to end up broke and out of work.

In 1930, Wm. H. Murray was elected the ninth governor of the State of Oklahoma. By 1933 his arrogance had pushed him through a futile run for the presidency of the United States. He developed a special hatred for the man America had chosen, the yankee President Franklin Delano Roosevelt – and for all of Roosevelt's projects to bring federal assistance to the suffering people in Oklahoma.

And all that is how Oklahoma, everybody's promised land, got so that a colored boy couldn't even lick his ice cream cone in a drugstore run by a white man in Eufaula, McIntosh County, Oklahoma. And so it was that Oklahoma in 1933 was a good place for some folks to simply get out of. It didn't take an education in the white man's schools to figure that out.

Hiding in the stinking weeds alongside the railroad track, the boy watched the open doors of the rail cars ease past him, slower and slower, until this particular one invited him in. With a gravel-scattering dash, he hauled himself aboard. And while the train jostled and the embers whipped in through the open door, the boy thought about Papa, the hardscrabble farm and old white Mr. Bob and neighbors who wouldn't let him sit at the table with them when his best little white friend asked him to dinner. And he thought about Roscoe Dunjee.

The train, feeling for the lowest and most direct route to the south and west, ran diagonally through Pittsburg County. McAlester was about 25 miles into the boy's journey away. Two or three miles south of McAlester there was a switch on the railroad called Frink's Switch. The train passed Frink's Switch in a hurry, carrying the boy on to the south and west, faster and easier than he had ever traveled in his life.

3

Peaceable Mountain

When this was Indian Country, McIntosh County and Pittsburg County were in two different nations. McIntosh was in the Creek Nation; Pittsburg County was created from old Tobucksy County in the Choctaw Nation. It took its name from Pittsburgh, Pennsylvania, out of admiration for all the coal that was mined there. Pittsburg County, Oklahoma, had been coal country since the white men found the coal there and leased it from the Indians and lured men of all colors from countries all over the world to come and dig it for wages.

McAlester is the county seat of Pittsburg County. The town was named for James J. McAlester, a prominent merchant and coal producer, member of the first Corporation Commission and second lieutenant governor of Oklahoma.

It was a long, hungry trip in a horse-pulled wagon from McAlester to Frink's Switch to a place called Peaceable Mountain – unless the man in the spring seat had money in his pocket and inclination to stop at Munn's store for baloney and cheese and lightbread. That seldom happened in 1933, but when it did, a farm boy sitting with his feet dangling over the back of that wagon could make it last for much of the seven miles of sand road that led from Frink's Switch to Peaceable Mountain. And he would remember the taste of it until the day he died.

The road to Peaceable Mountain led past the Pittsburg County Poor Farm, off to the right, there, giving parents a chance to point from the wagon's seat and to caution about the perils of not going to school, of being reluctant to work or of being wasteful. The poor farm was the last and only refuge for those who could not make it on their own. Few of the folks at the poor farm came from Peaceable Mountain. People there were of a kind that looked after the old folks until they died in their own beds.

A wagon on the way to Peaceable Mountain trundled across the end of Kiss Marie Canyon, where there was a spring of good water, pretty well hidden. Myriad wisps of woodsmoke rose from it during the 30s. There was a shortcut that lopped many a step out of the long walk to McAlester, but boys were told to stay out of the canyon and on the long road when the smoke wisps told them the whiskey makers were at their work.

Nothing much important ever happened at Peaceable Mountain. It wasn't on maps. Some said it was more a state of mind than a place. It wasn't much of a mountain at all unless you were climbing it after walking from McAlester or driving a Model-T Ford. Then it was a pretty good-sized mountain. Drivers would stop their Model-T Fords just past Peaceable Creek and turn around and back up the mountain so that gas would continue to flow down its gravity fuel system to its carburetor. All of which was of no great concern because in 1933 nobody on Peaceable Mountain owned a car except for one man who had married an Osage woman with a headright, and they bought a new car every year. So the size of Peaceable Mountain, like so many other things, was relative to the conditions under which you approached it. As one local philosopher put it: "Depends on how a man is traveling, how big a hill is."

Peaceable Creek ran along the near edge of Peaceable Mountain. It wasn't much of a creek, either, unless it was the biggest creek you had ever seen, and then it was a big creek, spanned by a steel bridge on which the wagon rattled announcement that you were nearing home. There was something special about Peaceable Mountain in the 1930s. The Great Depression had reached right out from McAlester and got a good hold on it, yet nobody seemed to want to leave.

Red-faced Irishman Dan Patty lived there with his quiet wife and a brood of kids in a log cabin he made from trees cut from land whose owner he did not know and shaped with his own hands. They were a nice family. Dan Patty had the only radio on the mountain, and neighbors could gather in and hear President Roosevelt's fireside chats about how things were going to be okay. The radio had arrived with an aerial and a ground wire and a mind of its own. It would begin to fade out at critical moments, and someone would have to jump up and draw a bucket of water from the well and pour it on the groundwire, whereupon the signal came in loud and clear again, sometimes in time for listeners to hear the climax of whatever drama they had been following throughout the evening.

The J.I. Stipe family lived nearby. Jacob Irvine Stipe was a most unusual man, tall, with an easy-going smile playing at the corners of his mouth. J.I was an amateur politician of the kind envisioned by the dreamers who first gave the field of politics its name and definition, which is the art of influencing governmental policy to the good. J.I kept his politics close to home, helping to elect county sheriffs and commissioners and other people whose quality as men – or lack thereof – directly affected his family. Seemed like he had always been a member of the school board at Cooper

School to which his kids walked until they sent the bus over the mountain and took them to Savanna.

J.I. was a worker. Bony, with huge knobby hands hanging like seasoned hickory toolhandles from shoulders leaned forward as if for work – sculpted into a slab-sided efficiency from a mixture of German-Irish genes hard-whipped in the brutality of the coal mines of Pittsburg County. When mine work wasn't available and the crops weren't needing work, J.I. dug ditches, hauled rock, dug post holes, hunted with his boys and sold possum, skunk, coon and mink hides enough to buy a few clothes. Anything that might raise the $150 to $200 a year required to put beans and cornbread on the table for his wife, Eva Lucinda, and their nine children: Marie, Claude, Jack, Eugene Earl, Clyde, Francis, Patrick, Loretta, and the baby, Mary Lou.

J.I. was born June 19, 1897, at Enterprise, Indian Territory. He was the sixth of nine children born to Francis Marion and Sarah Hawkins Stipe. He went to school in Alderson and at Cooper School on Peaceable Mountain. By the end of the tenth grade, it was time for him to take his turn in the coal mines, so he moved back to Alderson to be closer to them. After serving in World War I, he moved to Krebs and married Eva Lucinda Cable, and they moved back to Peaceable Mountain, where, as he said himself, he belonged. Grandpa Stipe lived up on the hill. J.I.'s family worked 160 acres down below. Grandpa was good to J.I.'s family, and they would go up and work out his crops for him.

Eugene Earl was the only kid who had black hair. Nobody called him Eugene Earl because he hated it. He had never known of anybody who amounted to anything whose name was Eugene Earl. His family mostly called him Injin Joe because of the Indian-like blackness of his hair. Other people just called him Joe unless he was sick or somebody was mad at him or something, and then they called him Eugene Earl.

The nearest fame had ever come to the Stipe family was the naming of a hill for them out to the south of Alderson. When J.I. was a boy, his family sold so much buttermilk from their hilltop home there that the little rise came to be known as Buttermilk Hill.

J.I. did have one brother who left the mountain and went to college. Uncle Oren went to Oklahoma A&M, and Henry Bennett, the president of the college took an interest in him and gave him a job at the Experiment Farm. It took Uncle Oren eight years of working and studying, but he graduated and came home and taught Joe how to graft a pecan slip onto a hickory bush and get a papershell pecan tree. And while he showed Joe about grafting, Uncle Oren told him about Dr. Henry Garland Bennett, his hero. Dr. Bennett was born over around Hope, Arkansas, in a log cabin like Dan Patty's and went on to educate himself and get a doctor's degree and take over Oklahoma A&M college and turn it into a modern university. And he had set up a network of county agents and county home demonstration agents and agriculture teachers to try to help rural folks live better through those hard times.

But for years when Joe thought about Henry Bennett and Uncle Oren the main thing he would remember was apples and oranges. For all the years of his life that he could remember, Joe had got a French harp at Christmas, until he finally graduated to a pocket knife. He never could learn to play the French harp, but he got one every year, anyway, because they were cheap and you could buy them in McAlester. But when Uncle Oren would come to visit at Christmas he would always bring one brown sack filled with apples and one filled with oranges. And there was plenty for everybody. So, Joe was inclined to agree with Uncle Oren about the heroism of Dr. Henry Garland Bennett, especially at Christmastime.

J.I. was a union man and a Democrat. In 1932, J.I. and his fellow miners struck the Pittsburg County mines seeking a pay raise to $5 a day. Governor Alfalfa Bill Murray sent in Pete Hanraty to see what was going on. Pete, the original organizer of most of the mining unions in Oklahoma, had been a member of the Constitutional Convention with Murray and had succeeded in getting coal mining mentioned in the Constitution more than any other trade. He was elected the state's first mining inspector. By the 1930s, though, Pete was just one of several mining inspectors working for the new elected commissioner. Pete died of a heart attack before he could report back to the governor, and Bill Murray, not knowing anybody down there he could trust, called in the National Guard. They marched up to the picket line as Pete Hanraty never would have done and took J.I. and his mining friends off the picket line and herded them out to the state prison and locked them up. No beds, no food. Just locked them up for the night and then turned them loose.

"No man's labor," Murray chided them, "is worth $5 a day."

It made a better union member of J.I., but it did not improve his opinion of Alfalfa Bill Murray, even if he was supposed to be a Democrat.

The Stipes were a close family, hard-working, and looked after to perfection by Eva Lucinda. She was a quiet, peaceful woman until somebody did something to one of her kids or said in front of them something that should have been left unsaid. Then she was not a quiet and peaceful woman.

When Marie, the oldest girl, started to school, she was so thrilled she hurried home and taught Claudie what she had learned that day. And Claudie taught Jack and Jack taught Joe, and so it went on down the line. It became a family tradition that each Stipe child, when enrolled in school, already knew what their brothers and sisters had been taught in the preceding years. Sometimes after a long day's work J.I. would take some of his boys and walk over to Dan Patty's cabin and they would listen to the radio.

Eva Lucinda was a Cable. There were a lot of Cables in Pittsburg County. Most of them on Peaceable Mountain. Ten girls and three boys in Eva Lucinda's family alone. Eva Lucinda's daddy didn't believe women ought to inherit anything. Their men, he said, ought to take care of them. Eva Lucinda's daddy accumulated a lot of land in his lifetime – most all of the land from up near the poor farm clear down to Blanco. And most of the land turned out to have natural gas under it. But the boys got it all when he died. And so, while her brothers' families became wealthy, Eva Lucinda's family had to go it on their own. J.I. Stipe never seemed to mind. He just kept on smiling and kept on going.

Copper Hill was kind of a little side hill off Peaceable Mountain on the road to the Stipe house. The dirt on it was the color of copper. That's where the Stipes' mailbox was after they finally got the rural route. Joe was given the job of walking the mile to the mailbox after all the other chores were done. Anything might be in it. Chickens could be ordered through the mail and arrive alive in a little compartmented cardboard box that could be hung on the mailbox. And if the Stipes ran out of coffee or sugar, the mailman would pick up some for them if somebody would leave him a note and the money in the mailbox. So nobody knew for sure what might be in the mailbox on any given day. But that wasn't what worried Injin Joe.

There was only one house between the Stipe home and the mailbox; it was about midway, and it was a long way from anything or anybody else. And it was old. And it was abandoned. Weeds grew to its eaves. And it was hanted. Everybody on Peaceable Mountain knew it was hanted. There were stories all over the mountain about what those hants would do to a boy if they caught him alone there after dark. Joe had no light to carry that would keep the shadows away. Trees grew close and leaned across the road. It would get so dark Joe was lucky to find the mailbox – if he could get there through the hants. Joe worried so much about the hants he finally went, as he did with most of his problems, to his older brother, Jack, who also was his best friend in the whole world. And, arm around his shoulder, fingers scissoring his cheek affectionately, Jack confided to his little brother the secret of eluding the netherworld:

"You stop one hundred yards on this side of it, Joe, and you get a deep breath. And then you run. Run as fast as you can. Run another full hundred yards on past it. If you run fast enough, the hants won't bother you."

Joe had swelled with confidence and pride to have such an older brother.

"Oh, one more thing, Joe."

"What?"

"You got to hold your breath. All the way."

Joe had never succeeded in holding his breath for the full 200 yards, but he had done well enough that the hants never bothered him.

J.I Stipe was a born athlete. Country baseball was big on Peaceable Mountain, and J.I. played it until he was 60 years old. If there still was sunlight when his work was done, he would walk two miles with the boys to slam a baseball so far it took a long time to find it. Hit it so hard the other country baseball players on the mountain got to calling him Popeye. J.I. had to hit the baseball that far because the mines had done something to his legs that made it hard for him to run.

There was this old boy over at Savanna who could throw the ball as fast as J.I. could hit it far. Could have been a major leaguer except he couldn't see. He would throw one close to the batter and that batter would back up so far he couldn't reach home plate even with the tip end of his bat. He was that afraid that old blind boy was going to bean him. Fear won J.I.'s team a lot of ballgames. When that didn't work, they tried something else.

Here's what they did one time.

They had a game scheduled with the little town of Pittsburg, over south of Peaceable Mountain. They went over to Pittsburg and told them they were going to have to call off the game because the catcher was paralyzed. His legs wouldn't work. Then, they went back over and got the game on again, saying he was going to catch out of a wheelchair. They rigged up a wheelchair and took him over there in it, and this guy caught the first inning in the wheelchair. Came his time to bat, everybody was itching with curiosity.

"That's alright, he can bat from it, too."

Not wanting to take advantage of a cripple, the pitcher threw him a soft little ball right over the plate, and the catcher jumped out of that wheelchair and hit that damned ball – hit a home run. Then, he ran the bases. They'd do stuff like that. Have fist fights over it. The biggest fight anybody on Peaceable Mountain could remember was between Joe's Uncle Oscar and an old boy named Claude Hawkins. Joe's Uncle Oscar was the umpire, and Claude was playing.

Claude had played in the Major Leagues. Joe's Uncle Oscar called Claude out or something, made a bad call as far as Claude was concerned and Claude announced to the crowd that he would whip him. So the ballgame stopped and the fight started. Both were just bulls of men. When they hit each other, you'd think a head was going to have to come off. They just kept slugging it until Joe's Uncle Oscar got all of it he wanted, reached over and got a crank out of a Model T, whomped Claude a couple of times. The fight was over, and the ballgame could go on.

They didn't have Queensbury rules on Peaceable Mountain. They just kind of whipped on each other. J.I. told Joe to remember that whenever he got fighting mad.

"Anytime you go to fighting, you just end up whipping on each other."

4

Boy in a Happy Hat

Fort Worth, Texas! Wade was feeling good. The last fears had disappeared into the reassuring rumble and rhythm of the train. He had met two new Negro friends in the boxcar. They told him the secrets of the road. And he told them about Roscoe Dunjee.

Roscoe Dunjee lived in Oklahoma City, and he said things hadn't ought to be the way they were for Negroes. He printed a newspaper that said that, and he wore a white shirt and tie and eyeglasses and a dark-colored suit with a handkerchief folded and tucked into the small pocket on its breast. And he sat in the front of buses with white people, no matter what the law said, and he rode beside them on trains. When Governor Murray said Negroes could not live north of a certain street in Oklahoma City, Roscoe Dunjee went right down and rented two houses and moved Negro families in, because Roscoe Dunjee looked white enough and was educated enough to be a high-class white. But Roscoe Dunjee was a Negro. Clear through.

When Wade's mother and father went to Oklahoma City on the bus, the boy went with them, and they left him at *The Black Dispatch* newspaper office where he hung around all day with Roscoe Dunjee, and Roscoe Dunjee would tell him stories. Lynchings he had seen. Whippings.

"Roscoe Dunjee would go down South..."

Squatting in the debris of the boxcar, Wade told his two new friends his favorite stories.

"...He was real light-skinned. You couldn't tell him hardly from a white man. He would go down South when they would have a lynching down there and he would stand around with the white people and listen to them talk and get those stories and then he would come back to Oklahoma and print them in his newspaper."

"A newspaper for Negroes?"

"A newspaper for Negroes."

His friends listened mouth open at such a Negro.

"They couldn't find out in the Deep South – Mississippi, Louisiana and Alabama down there – how the truth was gettin' out in Oklahoma. And so Roscoe said the last time he was down there, he was standin' and listenin' to the white folks, and there was a Negro walked past him real fast and whispered, 'Follow me round the corner.' And Roscoe he followed him round the corner.

"'They done found out you a Negro down here and you been picking up these stories down here and printing them in Oklahoma and they are getting up a mob to lynch you tonight.'

"Roscoe left from there a-runnin'. He could hear the train blowin', and he didn't have time to get him a ticket, and he just run and grabbed the handlebars and the white conductor was reachin' down to him and helpin' him up in there and kind of smilin' and laughin'.

"'You gonna miss all the fun,' he said to Roscoe, 'they goin' to hang a nigger down here tonight.'"

And the three boys laughed all the way into Fort Worth about Roscoe Dunjee putting it on those Mississippi crackers because he was so white.

"White conductor reachin' down there and pickin' him up!"

"Roscoe Dunjee was first to join the National Association for the Advancement of Colored People when it come to Oklahoma."

And the boy reached in his pocket, reverently, past the carefully wrapped wad of Mama's money and showed them the card that said Wade Watts was a bona fide member of the Youth Council of the Oklahoma Chapter of the National Association for the Advancement of Colored People even though it cost 50 cents a year to belong. Because, he told them, the world he wanted to live in was the world according to Roscoe Dunjee. And that is where he hoped this train was going.

"We don't get off this train, we don't know where we be goin'."

As the train slowed, the three of them jumped off and walked away from the tracks, talking happily of where all they would go and what great things they would do.

Major Seward was one of the best-known blacks in the history of Pittsburg County. He would have been called a colonel if he had been a white man. Major Seward was the blacksmith in McAlester. Joe liked to watch him hammer dulled plow points sharp again and to listen to him talk politics. J.I. dropped the boy and the plow off at Major Seward's when he and Eva Lucinda went to the grocery store to buy groceries.

Governor Wm. H. Murray honored white people who did heroic things or helped him get elected by naming them honorary colonels. When he wished to honor a Negro, he named him a major, so that he did not diminish the honor he did to whites by naming them colonels.

Major Seward was a most unusual Negro. He wasn't a farmer, and he didn't come to Oklahoma in a wagon filled with dreams looking for free land or a state of his own. He was trying to get from the South to the North in pursuit of the ideals of W.E.B. DuBois – intellectual Negro civil-rights leader who espoused full and immediate racial equality and in later life turned Communist and moved to Ghana – when his car broke down in McAlester, and by the time he could get it fixed he had decided to stay. He rented a building and put his tools inside and went to work as the town blacksmith. And black politician.

That was about the time Bill Murray had come back from his failed Aryan gentile colony in South America and started politicking for governor again. Something about the old man in his wrinkled, ill-fitting suit, the cheese-and-cracker meals he ate on the road, and his constant preaching that the family farm was the cure for all that ailed America appealed to Major Seward. And old Bill Murray was saying some things about the Negro that he never would say before. He said that the Negro's greatest weakness was his gullibility and the ease with which a white man could fool him, and Major Seward knew that to be a fact. And he said if a Negro owned a piece of his own land and worked it, he would cast a better vote than many white men. And Major Seward knew that to be a fact, too. And those two statements were more in favor of the Negroes than any other white men were saying. After he got his car fixed, Major Seward got him an old trailer to talk from and a microphone and amplifier and he would run an electric cord from a black business out into a black street and he would get up on that trailer and talk for Alfalfa Bill Murray.

How it was that Major Seward set out to find the elegant black integrationist William Edward Burghardt DuBois and found the crude, white shaper of Jim Crow laws William Henry David Murray must remain a mystery of the human psyche. When black folks would argue with him that Bill Murray was a red-neck, cracker, fire-breathing segregationist, Major Seward would explain it this way in private. Being the kind of man he was he never would have talked that way in public.

"Well," he'd say, "we don't have a hell of a choice. W.E.B. DuBois is not on the ticket. If you find a white man that may slap you, and he's running against a white man who's going to take a boot and put it in your ass, you're going to go for the fella who'll slap you."

Sometimes, he said, such a man as Murray will help the Negro more accidentally than somebody else would ever do on purpose. And Major Seward figured the odd old white man in the wrinkled suit would do no worse than slap the Negro around a little bit. When Murray won the office of governor, he named the politicking blacksmith an honorary major for helping him so much and so the Negro blacksmith Seward became Major Seward and the name stayed with him until he died, so much that people came to forget his real first name.

"Hey, boy!"

It was a policeman, hurrying down the railroad tracks toward Wade and his two new friends.

"Yessir."

"Come over here."

"Yessir."

"What's your name?"

"Watts, sir, Wade Watts…"

And the policeman hit him.

Just as he was about to say he was Charlie Watts' boy, and his daddy owned his own 15 acres just outside Eufaula and he…

It knocked the boy down, his feet scuffling involuntarily in the gravel. He stared, stunned from the ground. His hat knocked silly on his head.

"Do something with that hat, boy."

Wade struggled to his feet, trying desperately to straighten the offending hat. The policeman hit him again. Knocked him down.

"I said do something with that goddammed hat, boy!"

Wade stood up again. His nose was starting to bleed. He pulled the hat down from the jaunty angle that had, only moments before, reflected the wonderful world according to Roscoe Dunjee. Pulled it clear down to his ears, cottonfield style. And the policeman knocked him down again.

"Pull it off!"

The boy barely heard the urgent whisper above the ringing in his ears. He looked around foggily and saw for the first time that his two new friends had their hats removed from their heads and tucked respectfully under their arms. And Wade pulled off his hat as his father had done at the bank in Eufaula. And he put it under his arm as the other boys were doing there along the railroad tracks in Fort Worth, Texas. And the policeman stopped hitting him.

5

Little Bitty Watermelons

By Phoenix, Arizona, Wade's nose had stopped bleeding. The three new friends had split three different ways when the policeman finally gave them permission to run. Wade had 35 cents left of his Mama's washing money, and he was hungry again. He found a park not far from the railroad tracks where the faces were black and reassuring. He sat down on a park bench and waited for something good to happen. Several men were squatting in a shady circle under a big tree.

"What they doin' over there?"

Wade asked it of the man sitting beside him on the bench.

"They gamblin'."

"Doggone."

"You ever gambled any, son?"

"No."

"They say that anybody ain't never gambled none, usually they just as lucky as they can be."

"Doggone."

Wade went over to watch.

And within 15 minutes the 35 cents was gone, and the world was no longer according to Roscoe Dunjee, and the inside of the boy's own head turned on him.

"Great big old ignorant, dumb black boy a thousand miles from home and hungry and don't know nobody and ain't got no money."

And he looked around for a rock to kick, but there was none. He began to cry. Big child's tears running hot through the coal grime that had collected on his face.

"Give that boy his money back. Don't do him like that."

It was the man from the bench.

The gambler paused, knee still on the ground, feeling the heat of the dice in his hand. He looked over the man. Looked over the boy.

"Damn that kid," he said, "I got my living to make."

Alfalfa Bill Murray called out the National Guard 34 times during his administration. He defended a Red River Bridge from Texas, shut down oil wells to try to keep up prices and arrested union men off the picket line. The Oklahoma National Guard was the most powerful force available to Murray, but it could do nothing about what was happening in Oklahoma. Things just kept getting worse. Worse even than in the country as a whole.

On Peaceable Mountain, Joe Stipe's left leg quit working. Nobody knew why it quit working. It just quit. Like the country's economy. The stock market. The boy came up a cripple. Leg hurt so bad he couldn't hoe corn, chop cotton, play baseball. Nothing. Not even walk to school.

The only way J.I. had to get Eugene Earl to a doctor was to hitch the horses to the wagon and start down that long sand road for McAlester. Half-day in, half-day back, and no work done. But J.I. just kept hooking the team to the wagon and loading up Eva

Lucinda and Eugene Earl and going to town until the doctors said they didn't know what to do but cut in there and try to see what wasn't working. Eva Lucinda put her foot down. No doctor was going to cut into one of her kids when they didn't even know what they were cutting for. J.I. and Eva Lucinda took their boy home and put him to bed. And the teacher sent home the *Book of Knowledge* to keep him occupied. And Eugene Earl read it. Front to back. And remembered most of it. And that became a habit with him.

One thought kept creeping scarily into his sickroom. When they brought in the crutches he knew they were getting close to asking him to take back up his rightful chore and go to the mailbox again. He would glance up often from the *Book of Knowledge* to those crutches propped beside his bed. And he would try to imagine holding his breath and running 200 yards with them tucked beneath his arms. He would shake his head and go back to his reading. No way he could outrun those hants on those crutches.

Alfalfa Bill Murray even turned the lawn of the state capitol into a potato patch and let hungry men work it for the potatoes to prove to the yankee dandy President that Oklahomans could do for themselves no matter how bad times got. And he formed corps of foragers to go into the countryside and gather up leftover vegetables from farmers. But things in Oklahoma just kept getting worse.

Wade rode broke to California. Los Angeles. Too hungry and too scared to be impressed with the enormity of that city. In desperation, he approached a white man on the street. The white man actually put his hand on the boy's shoulder.

"Son, I don't have any money, but down on 16th street they got a soup line down there and you can get some soup."

It was only fifteen after nine in the morning and already it was more people than the boy had ever seen and all of them in that line. Then it was noon, and he was still in line. With his stomach gnawing at his backbone, he finally was within three people of the fine-smelling kettle. They ran out of soup. Packed up the kettle and hurried away, with everybody yelling, leaving him standing there. It was late. People were starting to go home from work. Stores starting to close.

The boy went into a grocery store and begged, hat under his arm. The grocer gave him some old bread and the tied and drying ends of several baloney sticks. The boy ate them and sat down and wrote his first letter home.

"Dad, I am broke. Please send me a ticket so I can come home."

The answer took a week.

"Son, I don't have no money."

Franklin Delano Roosevelt was everything Bill Murray despised. A patrician governor of yankee New York who smoked cigarettes in a long holder and grinned during hard times. Talked warm and fancy on the radio. And believed big federal government could solve Oklahoma's problems.

Roosevelt had brushed aside Murray's grass roots presidential campaign in 1932, labeling him a hayseed and "as crazy as a bedbug." Oklahoma and the nation had sided with Roosevelt.

When the new President had first come into office in 1933, he had called Congress into special session, and immediately began proposing public work programs and federal help so people could, at least, earn their own food. Bill Murray fought it all. And so it was that help arrived slower in Oklahoma than it did in some other states.

Coming home from the opposite direction, the steam engine barreled through Canadian on a downhill grade and roared on out of Pittsburg County and through Eufaula at a speed that turned trackside weeds and rocks into a lethal blur into which Wade dared not jump. He had survived the week in California waiting to hear from his daddy by begging scraps from stores, and by hanging around the railroad tracks where field hands loaded watermelons and cantaloupes onto the trains. The fieldhands would break one from time to time, and they would laugh with glee when a hungry boy darted in and whisked it away. Now, Wade sat dangling his legs from the opened door of the boxcar, waiting for the train to slow to a walk going into Onapa. As he knew it would do from picking berries along the tracks with his Mama.

When he sat up from tumbling in the trackside weeds, ten miles of dusty road lay between him and Mama's cooking, but it wasn't the walk that he dreaded. Scared and lonesome and hungry as he was, the boy dreaded facing Charlie Watts.

Back in the 1920s when Alfalfa Bill Murray was trying to start an Aryan gentile farming colony in Bolivia, Charlie Watts had been in Canada trying to raise some wheat. A lot of Oklahoma blacks went to Canada, starting in 1908 when Oklahoma started putting its racial beliefs into new state law.

"We have no desire to do the Negro an injustice," Murray explained. "We shall protect him in his real rights.... We must provide the means for the advancement of the Negro race, and accept him as God gave him to us and use him for the good of society. As a rule, they are failures as lawyers, doctors and in other professions. He must be taught in the line of his own sphere, as porters, bootblacks and barbers and many lines of agriculture, horticulture and mechanics in which he is an adept, but it is an entirely false notion that the Negro can rise to the equal of a white man in the professions or become an equal citizen to grapple with public questions.... I doubt the propriety of teaching him in the public schools to run for office or to train him for professions..."

Then his face would turn dark.

"When a Negro says to me, 'Set 'em up,' or taps me on the shoulder as he would an associate or an equal friend, I would want to land on his chin. But when he comes to me with his hat under his arm, humbly saying, 'Cap'n' or 'Boss' give me a cigar, I would give it to him if it required the last cent I had with which to purchase it."

Charlie had heard that kind of talk before. He had missed being a slave by two years. His mama was a slave, but his father wasn't. His daddy was the white son of a slavemaster. And that son of a slavemaster watched Charlie Watts' mama and their oldest son sold off at a slave auction. The young white man bid on his black family until the price got to a thousand dollars, and then he had to watch them go. At least that was the legend the Watts family carried with them in their wagon when they fled to Oklahoma to get away from that sort of thing.

Charlie had hacked out a 100-acre farm on Kiamichi Mountain, just across the Kiamichi River from Albion and rode it out there until 1919, the year Wade was born. But Oklahoma had done what Bill Murray said they should do. Charlie sold the farm and hand-hewn cabin for $6,000 and headed north where he had been told blacks were equal to whites and crops grew tall, and money flowed freely. And it looked for a while as if it were going to be true. Charlie Watts coaxed 13,000 bushels of wheat from that Canadian land in a year when wheat was selling for 88 cents a bushel. More than $11,000, almost twice what he had sold his old farm for. In one crop, Miz Watts!

"Don't sell now, Watts, it's going to a dollar. Don't sell."

Friends he trusted told him that. So Charlie didn't sell. Waited for $13,000.

Wheat fell to 75 cents.

"Don't sell, Watts. It's gonna go to a dollar yet. Don't sell, Watts."

When wheat got to 50 cents, Charlie Watts got so mad he said he wasn't going to sell his wheat at all. Feed it to the mules first. But he had to. He sold the whole crop for $1,690. Thirteen cents a bushel. It broke him. He collected all he could get together and returned to Oklahoma and worked the coal mines for $1.25 a day until he could buy the 15 acres and the old house just outside Eufaula in McIntosh County.

Since getting his son's letter from California, Charlie Watts had found more and more reasons to be on the front porch along toward evening where he could look a long way down the road and see if somebody was coming. Charlie Watts didn't like to mix in when his wife, Miz Watts, was handling the kids, but ever since watching the boy's slender form grow smaller going down the road, he had wished that he had. Best plowhand he had ever had.

Wade wouldn't go right down through town. The gravel had cut all the sole out from under his shoes, leaving only the tops flopping. He sneaked down a side street, and there was a mudhole there, and he was so tired he tried to jump it instead of walking around, and when his foot landed on the other side, the shoetop slid clear up around his knee. He pulled it back down over his foot and slunk on home. His dad was sitting on the porch, studying a pile of little bitty, dry-weather watermelons he had just brought in from the field. The two exchanged the small talk men share when neither wants to say what he is thinking.

"Miz Watts and the kids in town."

The boy slid through the talk and into the kitchen, sidled over to the stove, looking over his shoulder to be sure Charlie Watts wasn't seeing the truth of what he had told the boy before he left. His hand trembled on the door of the stove's oven. There was nothing in there. He tiptoed over to the ice box and eased its door open. And nothing was in there. Even the ice had melted. Everybody had eaten everything. There were no Mama's leftovers.

He leaned against the ice box, thinking about the little bitty watermelons. He walked casually back onto the porch, pulled out his pocketknife and cut one of them as if politely passing the time of day. And he ate it. Cut another. Ate it, and with the pain eased, he picked up the rinds and went around to the hog pen and threw them to the hogs, and when he stepped back around the corner of the house, the most beautiful picture he had ever seen greeted him. His mama and sisters and little brother, Buddy. Walking down the road. Old Oklahoma corn patch on each side.

Charlie Watts stood up. Hollered.

"Hey, Miz Watts! Ol' Wade done come back here and he's about to starve to death! He done searched this house over for something to eat and couldn't find it, he done come out here and eat up six watermelons."

And Charlie Watts sat down hard in the rope-bottomed chair that had been tilted against the wall and laughed until tears wet the field dust that had collected that day in the crinkles at the corners of his eyes. The boy nudged angrily at the farmyard with an exposed toe.

"Didn't eat but two of the little old things."

After she had fed him, his mama went into the note money and gave him two dollars and forty eight cents, and into her sewing basket for a tape measure. She made him stand on the tape-measure to be sure of his foot size because once a Negro put a pair of shoes on his feet in Eufaula, Oklahoma, he could not put them back on the white man's shelves. And this family didn't need to be spending no money on no shoes nobody could wear, at least until little Buddy could grow into them.

6

The Train to Oklahoma City

J.O. Rich was a fine old school master who in 1934 was winding down a wonderful career in education by serving as Superintendent of Schools of Latimer County. But there was this problem that kept nagging at him and would not let him rest. It finally bothered him so bad he put on his best clothes and got on a train and went all the way to Oklahoma City to see if he couldn't do something about it.

Latimer County lies to the east of Peaceable Mountain and south and east of Eufaula. It, too, is in the old Choctaw Nation. It, too, was coal country until a tremendous explosion in 1926 forced most of the mines to close. Cattle raising and farming took over. Latimer County was named for James S. Latimer who served in the Oklahoma Constitutional Convention and helped to lay out the county. It is more hill country than Pittsburg or McIntosh, edging closer to the last uplift of the Ozarks spilling into Oklahoma from Arkansas and Missouri. Latimer County's 728 square miles stitch

Elijah Thomas Dunlap

together the San Bois mountains, northernmost of the Ouachitas, with the Kiamichis and Winding Stair.

State Highway 270 runs east and west across the north-central part of Latimer County, and in the weeds of its right of way the seeds of what is called civilization took root earliest. A community called Cravens once lay about halfway between Red Oak and Wilburton, four miles south over the mountain from the highway and civilization. Cravens really was Brown Prairie, named after a man who helped found it, but when the post office came, the federal postal people declined the name and it was rechristened Cravens after a railroad official. The most important statistic of all that to this story is that Cravens was seven hard horseback miles from the nearest schoolbus. But that wasn't what was bothering J.O. Rich. Well, sort of.

Until 1934 or so, people wanting to be rural school teachers in Oklahoma could be certified in three stages after graduating from high school because the odds were so small that they would ever be able to go on to college to advance their learning of that important art. Upon graduation from high school, a would-be teacher took an examination prepared by the State Board of Education and administered by the county superintendent of schools. If the student passed it, he or she was issued a third-class certificate which allowed him or her to teach in limited situations. After a year of successful teaching and a summer course at a normal school, a hopeful could take another examination and be issued a second-class teaching certificate which authorized teaching in more situations. Upon completion of another year of teaching and another summer in normal school, a high-school graduate could take a third test and receive a first-class certificate and could serve in about any rural school situation. In 1934, the state was trying to do away with that sort of thing and force would-be teachers to go to college. And that was what was bothering J.O. Rich. And that is why he got on the train on that hot summer morning and started for Oklahoma City. He had this problem with this kid.

His name was Elijah Thomas Dunlap, named for the prophet and his daddy Lum's twin brother, Tom. Elijah Thomas was born on Dec. 19, 1914, on a ranch over the mountain in the Cravens community. He was among 16 children who lived sparely in a 14-room, two-story ranch house with his mom and dad. Thirteen children were from the marriage and the father had brought three daughters to it with him. In summertime, the family ran cattle on the free range back in the mountains and grew feed against the winter. Come late fall, Elijah Thomas and his dad would ride the mountains searching for the family cows, herd them up and bring them in to pastures near the house, along with the new calves that had joined the herd in the late spring. The following spring, they would burn the family brand onto the flanks of the new calves and turn them out to run free in the mountains until fall, selling off at some point enough cattle to pay the family's bills.

Elijah Thomas attended a two-room, two-teacher rural school a quarter-mile from the ranchhouse. The school had about 100 students in eight grades, divided into "the little room" for children in the first four grades and "the big room" for pupils from grades four through eight. Elijah Thomas's father died the year the boy turned 14, leaving seven children at home with their mother, of whom Elijah Thomas was the oldest surviving son. He became the man of the family. First thing he did was to stop people calling him Elijah Thomas and go to calling him E.T. At age 15, E.T. was one of four kids in the graduating class of Cravens Elementary of 1929, and he was the only one who got a chance to go on to high school. E. T. Dunlap would never forget that.

The only things rarer than high schools in the Latimer County mountains were school buses to get kids to them. When it came time to go to high school, E.T. went to live with an older sister in Wewoka, but he got so homesick and concerned for his mama and the mountains that he packed up and got on the bus and went home within a week.

A man named Jay Pepper operated a country store in the community of Panola, four miles down a country road from the ranch and then three more miles west along the highway. The Dunlap family traded there and had become good friends with Jay Pepper. A school bus came to the front door of Pepper's store every school-day morning, a little Model A Ford designed to pick up the few lucky kids who lived close to the highway and take them into Wilburton where there was a high school. Knowing E.T. and how he was, and being a good friend of the family, Jay Pepper offered the use of his horsebarn and lot if the boy wanted to go to high school bad enough to ride the seven miles every day on horseback. And the boy did. Rolled out of bed on bitter-black winter mornings in time to saddle his horse and get on the road by 5:30. Rode the seven miles through sleet, sometimes, or freezing rain that glued his glove to the saddle horn to get to Jay Pepper's store where he unsaddled the horse and put it into the barn and saw to it and then ran to catch the little bus and ride it another five miles into Wilburton – just to get into a school district that had a high school.

By E.T.'s sophomore year, the family had managed to buy its own Model A Ford, and E.T. got somebody to teach him how to work the gears and brake and clutch and he herded it down the dirt road and on to Wilburton. His high school education was going fine until one spring morning in his junior year when he woke up and couldn't move.

Rheumatic fever, the doctor said, caused by infected tonsils. E.T. was in bed for three weeks before he could even get well enough to be taken to McAlester and get the offending tonsils removed. By that time he had missed the final examination, and the doctor told him to stay in bed around the clock for another year if he wanted his heart to mend well enough to have any kind of normal life. It looked like the end of the boy's education. But the principal at the Wilburton High School – like Mr. Pepper – knew what kind of boy he was, and he waived the

final examination and gave him his grades. It was summer again before he was permitted to be out of bed for 12 of the 24 hours of a day. One of his sisters had moved to Red Oak, and he decided to go stay with her family and finish out his education there.

Red Oak was a small-town school district of about eight square miles and a senior class of 21 students. E.T. awoke to his world there: research, analysis, details, government issues, the history of anything. The Red Oak Class of 1934 elected him president. His debate teacher was John Prock, and he had a lot to do with that awakening, and a strong and lasting friendship grew to supercede the teacher-student relationship.

The year he graduated, E.T. drove over to an all-day church singing at LeFlore and met a girl named Opal Jones. They married after graduation. They had little money and no prospects of going on to college, no matter how smart they were. And that was the boy J.O. Rich was so worried about in that summer of 1934 that he got on the train and went all the way to Oklahoma City.

Caddo County is a long way from Peaceable Mountain and Cravens and Eufaula, the cradling hills of southeastern Oklahoma's old Indian Territory. Caddo County is out west where the soil turns red and flattens on its way to becoming the Great Plains, interrupted in its course, occasionally, by bright red gashes of unexpected canyons and upthrusts of multi-colored stone. Clear out in the western part of what originally was the old Chickasaw Indian Nation before it was taken from the Chickasaws after the Civil War as punishment for siding with the Confederacy. The land was used to settle wild Indian tribes and land-hungry whites. It was given to the whites by lottery rather than a repeat of the violent land runs that settled the first lands to the east. Caddo County is cattle country, and in the farm fields there peanuts begin to give way to alfalfa, from which old Bill Murray got his nickname, and to wheat. Caddo, in Indian, means "life."

In 1906, Caddo County was a part of Oklahoma Territory which was, at that time, presided over by a Republican governor named Frank Frantz. He had been appointed Oklahoma territorial governor after service as a "Rough Rider" under Col. Theodore Roosevelt who had since become President of the United States.

It was a busy year in history, 1906. The great San Francisco earthquake killed 503 people, and the first human voice boomed from Brant Rock, Mass., to ships a hundred miles at sea without benefit of wires or anything that could be seen. Autocar Company of Ardmore, Pennsylvania, added acetylene headlights and kerosene side lamps to their automobiles, but they didn't see how the rudder could be improved on for steering. Woodrow Wilson, the brilliant young president of Princeton University said the arrogance of the motor car was kicking up more than dust on its trips through the countryside. It was, he said, spreading resentful feelings that could turn rural America socialistic. He said it was a symbol of the arrogance of city wealth with all its carelessness. *The North American Review* added that more Americans had been killed by motorcars in five months than had died in all of Teddy Roosevelt's Spanish-American War.

A child named Lloyd Edwin Rader was born in August of that year in Bridgeport in northern Caddo County. Neither cars nor earthquakes nor voices floating through the air were any problem in Caddo County, but before Lloyd Rader could reach the age of eight, a horse he was riding rolled over on him and crushed his ribs and severely damaged his right lung. Because of that and the frail health of his mother, Lloyd Rader learned early the high cost of needing help when there was none around. Because his mother was sick much of the time, he and his little brother, Dean, assumed a lot of the responsibility there in the Caddo County farmhouse that kids usually don't have to assume. It developed in Lloyd Rader in childhood a consuming interest, some said it was an obsession, to look out for other people. Try to see that they had help when they needed it.

He graduated from Hinton High School in 1924, and attended Southwestern Oklahoma State University in Weatherford. He went to work as the assistant secretary for the Building and Loan Association in Weatherford in 1925.

By the time Alfalfa Bill Murray had come back from Bolivia and started his speaking tour that turned into a cheese-and-cracker political campaign for governor, the automobile had come into its own even out in Caddo County, and it carried no residual hints of being an inspiration to socialism. About one in five people owned a car, but not everybody knew how to drive one.

That was when and how old Alfalfa Bill Murray happened to meet a bright young man who was working as assistant secretary for the Building and Loan Association in Weatherford. The most attractive thing about this young man to Murray was that he could drive a car. And he would. The young man drove Murray all over western Oklahoma to campaign, and he listened to what the old man had to say. And much of it he liked. Especially about methods of administration. In 1932, when the Hoover Administration authorized tiny relief checks to farmers forced off their land, Murray named the young man relief director of Custer County, just to the northwest of Caddo. And that was the first time Lloyd Rader's passion for helping people who needed help came to national attention in the form of a tent city on the Washita River near Clinton, filled with starving farmers and their big-eyed children. The number of relief checks Rader distributed sent waves all the way to Washington.

Later, the building and loan association for which Rader worked collapsed in the depression and put him out of work. He went to Bill Murray in desperation, and Murray got him a job in Oklahoma City working for the new Oklahoma Tax Commission that Murray had just created.

1936

The distant thunder of hate in Europe grew nearer. Italy had thrown in as a partner with Hitler's rampaging Germany and to show good faith killed hundreds of thousands of barefoot Ethiopian warriors with bombs and mustard gas. Benito Mussolini's son-in-law Conte Galeazzo Ciano was enraptured at the beauty of bombs "opening like red blossoms" on Ethiopia's highlands.

Ethiopian Emperor Haile Selassie appeared, tiny behind the podium, to appeal to the League of Nations for help. He sensed it would not come.

"It is us, today," he murmured, "It will be you tomorrow."

Josef Stalin started liquidating political enemies in the Soviet Union in a Great Purge that would take eight to ten million lives before it was over.

In America, President Roosevelt won resounding re-election to a second term. The Bureau of Labor Statistics placed the poverty line at $1,330 a year. Thirty-eight percent of U.S. families – 11.7 million – made less than $1,000.

In Oklahoma, farmers still figured they had to put together about $200 to make a crop and live out the year.

7

A Most Heartbreaking Year

Nineteen hundred and thirty six was the most heartbreaking year anybody on Peaceable Mountain could remember. Rain stopped. Corn leaves dried before ears made. Stalks bowed pitifully before a persistent hot wind. Old folks and babies began to die. There was no help anywhere. It was more, almost, than a man could stand.

Moonshine fires burned steadily near the good spring of water up in Kiss Marie Canyon, and bottled hope was loaded onto cars and trucks down where the road from town crossed the canyon. Constant lines of pitiful people waited before the doors of legislators, county commissioners, anybody who might have access to a job. One state legislator was besieged by so many pitiful people he started getting up early every morning, and he and a jug of good Kiss Marie Canyon whiskey would get in his boat in the dawn dark and row out to the center of the lake where they would fish together and try to figure some way out of the helplessness until dark arrived. And then the man would come back in alone. Sneak into his own home.

People who had never darkened a church door began ganging up in the little white frame backwoods chapels. Hunger struck fiery eloquence from the souls of old country boys who discovered you could get a quarter for groceries from a man in church, sometimes, when you couldn't get it from him anywhere else.

Others dreamed of gold. Hidden treasures. Jesse James' hidden bank sacks. Belle Starr. So far as is known, nothing was ever found in dark caves and undersides of rocks except maybe some hope for a little while, and, after all, that was what everybody was looking for.

The only good news on the mountain that year was that Eugene Earl was up from the bed being called Injin Joe again. Hadn't died. Wasn't crippled. Limped a little, one leg slightly shorter than the other, but he could outrun the hants to the mailbox again. Everybody on the mountain called it a miracle.

J.I. and Eva Lucinda finally had found an old black doctor someone on the mountain had heard about. A kind of a black civic leader in McAlester, he had been forced to go to the East to get his medical degree because the only college for blacks in Oklahoma was Langston, and Langston taught only what Oklahoma thought Negroes needed to know. And that was how to farm and how to teach other blacks to farm. Wickham was the doctor's name.

"Yeast," he told Eva Lucinda, "two big glasses of powdered yeast mixed with water. Every day." All kinds of vitamins. And he hooked Joe up to a mysterious electrical contraption, and the boy would sit and hold onto it, and the mild electrical current would ripple through his body. It took a year, but it worked. The problem went away. Whatever it was. Nobody knew. Not even Dr. Wickham. Unknown diseases were common on the mountain. Folks learned to be grateful if the victim got out of bed instead of dying.

"We did what he told us to do," J.I. shrugged to Dan Patty one night sitting around the radio, "and it worked."

Other than that, good news was scarce as rain on Peaceable Mountain. Water ran out. None even for the livestock. Ponds dried up, and their bottoms cracked. Boils broke out on people.

The only person Joe knew who stayed happy through that summer was a kid named Leo Tibbs. Adults said Leo was off center just a little bit, wasn't quite right. But Joe knew it was something more than that. Bees and ants wouldn't sting him. Wasps wouldn't sting him. Leo and Joe would go out and chuck rocks at wasp nests, and the wasps would chase Joe down and sting him and everything and everybody else within reach except Leo Tibbs. They wouldn't bother Leo. Just as the drought didn't. The heat. Boils left him alone. Joe always believed there was a special kinship between Leo and something on the mountain that was too big for Joe to understand. Some kind of special understanding. Leo was the calmest person on the mountain that summer except, maybe, for J.I. Stipe. J.I. just kept getting up and going to work as if nothing else was going on. Nobody had ever seen J.I. Stipe get upset, except for a couple of times, maybe. Once when the National Guard hauled him off to prison during the coal strike, and then on that night back in 1935 when Jimmy Braddock knocked out Max Baer for the heavyweight boxing championship of the world.

Braddock had Baer on the ropes and the announcer and the crowd got to screaming so bad you could hardly hear anyway, and Dan Patty's radio started fading out, and J.I. got mad then. But he just grabbed for the bucket and ran for the well and drew water so fast the rope smoked and poured it on the groundwire just in time to hear history made. Clear back in on Peaceable Mountain, standing there with the bucket in his hand, he heard the referee count Baer out as the reigning heavyweight champion of the world, and saw in his mind's eye the raised hands of Jimmy Braddock. That

Left to right: *Back row – Eva Lucinda (holding Francis), J.I.;
Middle – Cousin Herbert McFadden, Jack, Marie; Front – Clyde, Joe,
Claudie.*

was kind of the way J.I. Stipe did things. Then his whole world
cracked and started falling into pieces.

Claudie died. His first-born son. Joe's oldest brother. The boy
came grinning home from another dark-to-dark day of trying to
salvage peanuts from a dried field and fell exhausted into his bed.
When Eva Lucinda got up to fix breakfast the next morning, the
stove was cold. And when she went to scold Claudie, she found
him dead in his bed. Sometime during the night, Claudie had just
quit breathing. Big, grinning Claudie, bringer of knowledge and

good humor from the outside world to the old farmhouse. J.I. and Eva Lucinda never even got a chance to hook up the team to the wagon and try to get him to town. And nobody knew why. It was whispered around the mountain that the boy had eaten some peanuts that were bad. Or too green or too many of them. Or something. But nobody knew. Nobody ever knew. It was just whatever it was out there that stopped the rain and brought the boils and shriveled the corn and took the joy from a mountain summer day. They laid Claudie out on a board in his best clothes and put him in the living room while neighbors hammered together a casket from new pine wood.

❖

Ernest Whitworth Marland had replaced Alfalfa Bill Murray as Oklahoma's governor on Jan. 15, 1935. Marland was a well-educated, gentlemanly oilman who had completed a term in Congress and a new mansion near Ponca City before hard times and financial chicanery cut him down. E.W. Marland was the kind of man who commissioned a statue to the pioneer women of Oklahoma instead of sitting for a self-portrait. He was a personal friend to President Franklin Roosevelt and had won election as Oklahoma's tenth governor on a promise to bring Roosevelt's New Deal relief – finally – to Oklahoma. And by mid-year 1936, he was getting desperate.

People all over the United States were getting help, but only a trickle of public works programs had come into Oklahoma. Alfalfa Bill had fought it bitterly as federal intervention in Oklahoma's affairs. And, Marland's own Democratic-dominated legislature fought everything he proposed, because, Marland suspected, of their lingering Murray-like view of the New Yorker Roosevelt. Marland had gone over the legislators' heads and to the people. He had circulated a petition which would allow Oklahomans to use their progressive constitution to over-ride their elected representatives, amend the constitution, set up a system to receive federal aid from Washington and tax themselves to pay their share. Businessmen challenged the petition's legality. Marland ordered the election anyway. Depression-weary Oklahomans approved it by a vote of 204,626 to 78,783. The businessmen went to court. The court overturned the election. And Marland and the folks who couldn't take care of themselves and those who wanted to help them were back where they were when he entered office.

❖

Seven-year itch broke out on Peaceable Mountain. Hell of a year. Everything failed.

Two of J.I.'s and Eva Lucinda's babies died. Like Claudie. Before they ever had a chance to know who they were. Joe's little brother, Patrick, and sister, Loretta. Nobody knew why. Lucinda was beside herself with grief and weakened by the birth of another child, baby Mary Lou. Death hovered like a plague cloud over a happy house. J.I. Stipe just kept getting up in the morning and going to work doing anything anybody would let him do to feed those who were left. Things could not get worse. But they did.

Eva Lucinda died. Mama. Source of all good things. And nobody could tell Joe why. They put her on that awful board and put her in the living room, and nightmares crept with the dark into Joe's bedroom. Four funerals in the J.I. Stipe house in one awful year.

The Stipes gathered. The Cables came, the twelve remaining brothers and sisters of Eva Lucinda. They looked at the six surviving youngsters and whispered. Their whispers chilled Joe. They were talking about who was going to take him home with them to live, and who was going to take his little brother Clyde and who was going to take his baby brother Francis and newborn Mary Lou. Because people on the mountain were going crazy over things less than what J.I. had been through. Walking off into the woods and living in caves. Slipping back into early childhood. Nobody wanted such a thing to happen to such a man as J.I. Stipe. So they decided to ease his load. Find other homes for his kids.

Fear knifed deeper than grief into ten-year-old Joe's empty belly. That chain of family affection and education and protection that nobody had ever questioned had suddenly gone to pieces like a dried dirtclod in his hands. Joe wandered about his chores in a daze. How could he live in somebody else's house? Without his daddy? Without Claudie? Without Jack, who also was his best friend in the world.

❖

Governor Marland tried again, more patiently this time. And in 1936, in addition to slapping down Marland's mid-term bid to jump from the governorship into the U.S. Senate, the people of Oklahoma added some words to that Constitution Bill Murray had protected in a tin box between his knees. The new words set up a Department of Public Welfare. Put a sales tax on whoever had any money to spend to raise funds to match federal money made available by the federal government for "relief and care of needy aged persons who are unable to provide for themselves and for other needy persons who, on account of immature age, physical infirmity, disability, or other causes are unable to provide for themselves...."

Lloyd Edwin Rader

One of the leaders in that 1936 petition drive was a young man from Caddo County, way west of Peaceable Mountain. A tall, striking young man, they said, with piercing eyes. Well employed as chief enforcement officer for the Oklahoma Tax Commission. With an obsession for looking after people who needed help. His name was Lloyd Edwin Rader.

On Peaceable Mountain, J. I. Stipe just kept getting up in the morning and going to the fields. Digging ditches for pay. Hauling rock to put cornbread and beans on a hushed dinner table. Joe's oldest sister Marie took over the cooking and became Mama as best she could. For Joe, it was like waiting for a storm that wouldn't break and wouldn't go away, just hung there over the mountain, threatening with little flickers of fear. He watched over his shoulder for the dust clouds of the wagons coming to take them away. And the end of every day was a relief when he could go to his own bed one more time in his own house and say goodnight to his own daddy. Finally, Joe couldn't take it any more.

He stood before his dad, hands on his hips, fear and anger trembling his lips, and he told J.I. of the whispers he had overheard. Asked him when the wagons were coming. To whom he would be given. J.I. Stipe looked stunned. He sat down hard. Put heavy, callused hands on his boy's shoulders. The frightened boy had not heard his father's answer to those who tried to help.

"Son," he said, "we aren't going to give anybody away."

Prettiest words the boy had ever heard. Like gentle rain drumming on a dry mountain.

8

Mr. Crawley's Gold

One thing Wade had known forever that he did not want to do for the rest of his life, and it was following a mule's tail with the corn leaves cutting blood from his ears. The year he turned 19, he figured out what it was that he did want to do. Wade Watts wanted to be a lawyer.

It started with this older kid. He was white. And he was smart. And he could talk. Wade met him at one of the informal wrestling matches where the Negro boys and the white boys gathered on the grass of a vacant lot near downtown Eufaula after their separate days at school. This kid would talk to Wade almost as if he were white. His name was Kirksey Nix, and Kirksey Nix was no wrestler. Polio or something had kept him from being strong physically, but something about the boy was impressive. Then Wade heard him really talk.

It was a public debate between Kirksey and another white boy. Wade had to sit at the back of the crowd out of the way, but that white boy's words could reach all the way back there and get right inside and churn things up. Kirksey went away to college to be a lawyer, and when he would come home on weekends, he would tell Wade how he was going to be a good lawyer. Make a lot of money, he said, but also help poor people and set the laws right. Kick hell out of some big guys. And Wade hung around and listened to his stories as he had hung around Roscoe Dunjee and listened to his. And that was when Wade decided he wanted to be a lawyer.

He got a job helping a farmer for fifty cents a day so he could start putting money away for his college education. He got in a half day before the work gave out. The man told him to come by his house on Saturday and collect his twenty-five cents. He walked the mile and a half, knocked respectfully on the door.

"He is sleeping," the man's wife told him. "You can't disturb him now. Come back later."

"I done walked a mile and a half and if I leave without my quarter, then I gotta walk a mile and a half home and then a mile and a half back here to get it."

"He's sleeping. You cannot wake him now."

He got a job mowing lawns. He was mowing a white woman's yard one evening when the newsboy bicycled past and threw the woman's newspaper onto the lawn. It landed in front of the mower. Wade picked it up, knocked on the door and handed it to the woman.

"Now, Wade," she said, "you ought to know better than that. Negroes always knock on the back door to a white person's home."

And so it was, Wade walked the dying-rose-colored road to Canadian again. Where the trains slowed to a walk, with their boxcar doors open and beckoning.

Three dollars a day! For pitching California watermelons. Fifteen dollars every Saturday. And every Saturday, he proudly counted out three dollars and mailed them home to his Mama. And he bought school clothes, and he tried them on, and if he didn't like them, he handed them right back and that California clerk hung them back on that rack where a white man was just as likely as not to buy one of them and put it on. And he tried on all the shoes he wanted to try on and handed them back, and he watched the California clerk put them back on the shelves. And being a lawyer seemed to edge a little bit closer with every passing day.

Wade followed the watermelons north. San Joaquin Valley, Blythe, Delano, Fresno. And when the summer was over, he hopped a freight home, and this time he walked right down through the middle of Eufaula wearing new shoes. With a bundle of new clothes under his arm. Head held up. Walking straight like his daddy did.

❖

On Peaceable Mountain, Mr. Crawley went crazy. He was a nice man, tall and pleasant, who lived over the mountain from the Stipes. Working in those hot, dry fields every day from dark to dark, he got it in his head that Jesse James had buried some gold in an old cave down near the cool, shady waters of Brushy Creek. He threw down his hoe and headed for Brushy Creek. Left his crop. Lived down there in that cave. Digging for treasure. People on the mountain shook their heads over him. Wives began watching their men for signs.

J.I. got his surviving boys up earlier than usual on the morning after they heard the frightened whispers, and they walked over the mountain to Mr. Crawley's place with their hoes on their shoulders. And sure enough, Mr. Crawley was gone, and the corn was going to weeds. They worked out his crop for him. Just like it was theirs. And when it needed working again, J.I. got the boys up early and they walked over the mountain and worked it out again, then walked back home and worked out their own.

Joe fumed. That old man down there digging for that treasure in the shade and the Stipes up here in the sun hoeing his corn and chopping his cotton! And when he found that gold, he was going to be rich, and the Stipes would still be hoeing corn and chopping cotton.

"It's what neighbors do," his daddy told him, and that was the end of that. Until the night Mr. Crawley showed up at the Stipe place.

"J.I.," he said, "I want to thank you for workin' out my corn and cotton. But it ain't going to be needed."

Joe's breath caught in his throat. Mr. Crawley leaned forward and his voice dropped so that Joe had to scurry to hear.

"Irvine, if you will come down and bring your boys and dig three days, we'll have that gold."

Joe's heart leaped. It was over! Hard times were done. It was the best business proposition he had ever heard. But his daddy just sat there. The family's whole future hanging in the balance, and Jacob Irvine Stipe just sat there. Finally, he spoke.

"I'll tell you what, Mr. Crawley..."

Joe couldn't breathe.

"... If you'll pay us a dollar a day, we'll come down there and dig and you can have all that gold."

Joe couldn't believe it. He stomped out the door and kicked rocks in the yard. After much such meditation out in the quiet under the cool, faraway stars, it finally came clear to him. Good a man as his daddy was, he sure didn't know anything about gold.

Charlie Watts got a job with the WPA, and by hiring out his mules, too, he drew $21 a month. Steady. No on-and-off stuff. Wade got a job cleaning up vacant lots for the WPA between summers. He made ten dollars a month and had time enough to go to high school. He worked late afternoons and Saturdays. Saved his money to be a lawyer. Went to school almost every day except during cotton picking which usually ended in November, except sometimes he stayed in the field to scrap a little leftover cotton for Christmas money. At night, he studied. And dreamed of practicing the law. Maybe with Kirksey. Maybe help Roscoe Dunjee set things right for the black folks. Maybe he and Kirksey and Roscoe... And he would drift to sleep on the first beautiful dreams of his life.

When school was out again, he hopped a freight for California and the watermelon fields. On May 5th, they started pitching watermelons in El Centro, in the Imperial Valley, nearly in Mexico. Then up through the San Joaquin Valley, then home again.

Kirksey graduated from college. Came home a lawyer. Ran for the state legislature in 1938. Won.

❖

In the spring of that year, John Prock, Red Oak schoolteacher, got to thinking about the kid named Elijah Thomas Dunlap, who had so worried J.O. Rich four years before. The reason J.O. Rich had made that long train trip to Oklahoma City back in 1934 was to plead with the assistant state superintendent of public instruction, A.E. Riling, to issue one last teaching certificate examination before the state closed the program down.

"It will give a young, bright kid down there a chance to get a third-class certificate so he can get into the school-teaching business and maybe earn enough money to go on to college. Otherwise, he'll probably never make it."

J.O. Rich had brought back that examination on the train from Oklahoma City and administered it to Elijah Thomas Dunlap, and the boy had passed the test and received the last third-class teaching certificate issued by the State Board of Education in Oklahoma. He had gone right to work teaching the kids in "the little room" of the two-room, two-teacher school in the Cravens Community where he had got his own elementary education. Fifty dollars a month for the five months the district could afford to keep the school open, discounted 5 per cent when he and his new wife, Opal, ran out of household money and had to ask for cash instead of waiting for the school warrants to come through. Then E.T. and Opal had moved over to the Norris School District, about eight miles east of Red Oak where they both taught. In addition to their teaching, E.T. and Opal alternated between summer courses at Southeastern State College in Durant and Eastern A&M in Wilburton and added Oklahoma A&M extension courses when they could get them. E.T., the boy who almost didn't finish high school, already was well on his way to a bachelor's degree. As J.O. Rich had known he would do if he was given a chance.

After thinking about E.T. Dunlap for a while, the kind of man he had become and all, John Prock called him down at Norris School, where the boy had already become principal at age 23, and asked him to meet him in Red Oak for lunch.

They met in Dick Lyons Café on a Saturday. Both ordered chili. Talked for a bit about how the elderly county school superintendent who had replaced J.O. Rich had managed to accumulate what E.T. called "a fairly respectable degree of unpopularity in the county."

It was shaping up to be a crazy political year, Prock told him. Nine Democrats, including two ex-governors, Wm. H. Murray and Jack Walton – who had been impeached after routing the Ku Klux Klan out of Oklahoma back in the early twenties – were scrambling for the Democratic nomination as governor. It was one of those years, he said, when anything could happen in any political race in any part of the state. Then there was a long silence.

"E.T.?"

Prock was poking with his spoon at the crackers in the chili.

"I think you ought to run for county superintendent of schools."

"Oh, golly, no, Mr. Prock, I'm too young. Don't you think?"

"No, you'd win it."

"I don't even have my bachelor's degree."

"You don't have to."

E.T. stuttered each protest with less conviction, and after he surrendered the two of them sat long over their empty chili bowls, scratching out dreams on the one clean napkin left from their chili.

"I think," said Mr. Prock, "we should concentrate on trying to do something to improve the school libraries."

But something else had long been building in E.T.'s mind.

"Every graduating elementary student in Latimer County," he said, "ought to be within schoolbus range of a high school, no matter how far back in the woods they live. If I am ever able to do anything, I am going to see that done."

9

Joe's Legendary Ham

Instinctively, Joe sat up in bed and looked out the window through the early morning to the smokehouse. His jaw dropped with amazement. J.I. was closing the smokehouse door. Walking off across the yard toward the gate with a ham on his shoulder. Joe scrambled out of bed. Burst out the front door and across the yard to stand in front of his father.

"Dad? Where are you going with our ham?"

And he asked it with an authority new to a 13-year-old boy.

Joe's oldest sister, Marie, had got married that year, 1939, and in most households that might have been a cause for greater celebration than it was in the Stipe home. When Eva Lucinda had died in 1936, Marie had stepped firmly into her role as caretaker and mama and cook and washerwoman and confidante in things feminine. All those things that only a woman can be. And Marie's marriage had left the house womanless. Cold again. All-male except for baby Mary Lou.

The loss had been softened for Joe by a new miracle. They had started sending a schoolbus across Peaceable Mountain from Savanna. It stopped right in front of the house. No more walking over to Cooper School at mid-winter in a worn ducking jumper with no lining. All the kids on the mountain wore ducking jumpers, and you could tell how well a family was doing by the kind of ducking jumpers their kids wore during those long walks down those country roads in bitter winter. If people were doing pretty good, you could pull open the front of one of those jumpers and there likely would be a lining under that ducking. Warm, fuzzy. But there weren't many lined ducking jumpers on Peaceable Mountain in 1939, and none of them hung behind the door in the J.I. Stipe household. Joe had got a job during his lunch hours fixing flats at the gasoline filling station in Savanna to try to help. The man who owned it charged a quarter a flat, and he gave Joe a dime to do the work. But that wouldn't start to buy a ducking jumper with a warm, fuzzy lining in it.

At home, Joe had become the cook at Marie's departure. Not through any comparison of abilities or inclinations, just harsh reality of survival on Peaceable Mountain. At 13, Joe still could not turn out the work his brother Jack could at age 15. The family lived better if Jack spent his time in the field and Joe spent part of his time in the kitchen. Joe surprised everybody. He reduced cooking to a system. Get up first thing in the morning and fill the old stove with wood. Put the beans on even before putting together some kind of breakfast. Last thing he'd do before running for the schoolbus was check those beans. Plenty of water in the pot. Plenty of wood in the stove. First thing he'd do when he got off the bus that evening was rebuild the fire in the stove, and by six, six-thirty, the beans would be done. He'd mix the cornbread, get it and the potatoes cooked, and supper was ready. His cornbread and fried potatoes began to rival those served in the houses of neighbors where wives and mothers still reigned.

Joe loved canned stuff, although about all of it he had ever tasted store-bought was tomatoes. There was a kid named O.D. Perryman whose grandpa had a store in Northtown. They had about 12 in the family, and they bought all their canned goods by case lots. They always had cases of canned tomatoes. When Joe and O.D. would go hunting, O.D. would swipe a can of tomatoes and they'd sit beside Peaceable Creek and share them. They were almost as good as baloney and cheese and lightbread eaten in a wagon trundling down the sand road from Frink's Switch.

Joe got excited when they announced at school that students were to go home and tell their mothers that Elizabeth Ford, county home demonstration agent, was going to teach the women how to can food with pressure cookers. Vegetables, fruit, meat. Joe went to the class, one teen-aged boy in a roomful of grown women. But he learned to can with a pressure cooker, and when Roosevelt's plan to drive up the price of beef cattle came to Peaceable Mountain, Joe figured a way to get the most out of it. The government would buy your cattle and come to your place and kill them. Leave them lying there. You could bury them or burn them or eat them, but you couldn't sell the meat. And when the government killed his daddy's cattle, Joe canned all the meat the Stipe family could afford to buy jars and lids for. Joe did grumble, but not about the cooking.

"Git Wood," he would say. "Git Wood. My name's Git Wood Stipe."

On mornings too cold even to go to school, the Stipes got wood. When it was too bad to do anything else, they got wood. You get on that crosscut saw, you wouldn't freeze. Your hands might get cold, but if you've got a pair of gloves to keep your hands warm, you're in good shape because the rest of you will stay warm on the end of that saw.

The fireplace was the only heat the family had other than that from the old cookstove, and in the bitterest cold of dead winter, heat from those two fires did not meet anywhere in between. Fireplace is the nicest thing in the world to see into. Evenings Joe could lie on the floor and look in there, and he could see Mr. Crawley's gold. But his feet would get to freezing and he would have to go get in bed to get warm all over at the same time.

There was an annual routine on Peaceable Mountain for keeping food for the family table. Every year as summer faded and fall came and the trees lost their leaves, people all over the mountain would begin watching the clouds, feeling the wind, checking their aches and almanacs for signs. And along in late fall or early winter the weather suddenly would turn off cold. That was hog-killing time. And you had to be ready. Men stayed home from outside work and kids stayed home from school and the importance of everything else paled before the importance of this day. And it was a happy day. Hard, long, bloody, exhausting. Happy. The smell of outdoor fires covered the mountain. Screams of terrified hogs echoed in the hollows. Steam rose from big iron kettles of water. The spat of .22 rifles and the profuse flowing of blood from the throats of stuck hogs were anything but frightening to a kid on Peaceable Mountain. They meant pork chops on the table. There was something mighty encouraging about storing up all that meat although you knew from the past that it would be gone before winter was. They killed the hogs and scraped off the hair, and suddenly the hogs weren't hogs any more. They were meat. Folks cut it up and got it quickly into the smokehouse and got the smoke and salt on it before the weather turned off warm enough for it to spoil. Fresh, fried pork chops, fatback for beans, bacon, ham. They had meat until they ran out. And then they did without except for what they could hunt or trap.

On a lonesome kind of Friday evening in that late winter of 1939, Joe went to the smokehouse and confirmed what he already knew. One ham hung there. Saved for the bitter end. He decided to end it with a bang. One big happy feast before everybody started getting lean and meat-hungry again. He would cook a Sunday dinner that everybody named Stipe would remember forever. It would become legend on Peaceable Mountain. The Sunday Injin Joe cooked the last ham of winter. He had gone to sleep that Friday night planning that famous Sunday dinner. And that is why he woke early on that Saturday morning and looked instinctively toward the smokehouse. And that is why he dared stand his ground now in front of his father.

"Dad? That's the last ham we got!"

J.I. met his eyes.

"I'm going to take it over and give it to Dan Patty, Joe."

"Why would you give our last meat to Dan Patty, Dad? I was planning it for Sunday dinner."

"We can eat something else for Sunday dinner, son. Their cabin burned down last night."

And the only way Injin Joe got a piece of that legendary ham was to go over to Patty's place on that Sunday to visit at just about noon. Mrs. Patty served him some of it for the Sunday dinner they ate in the tent they had put up near the black ruins of their cabin.

❖

Buffalo Valley is east and south of Peaceable Mountain, a whole county away. It is a beautiful strip of flat ground, 25 or 30 miles long, a great, rich agriculture valley and it lies along the foot of Buffalo Mountain deep in the old Choctaw Nation, west of Talihina and south of Wilburton in Latimer County. In the late 1930s, no school buses went down there.

Some areas of old Indian Territory civilized more slowly than did others, even after statehood came with its alleged improvement of conditions. It happened for many reasons. Sometimes because of remoteness. Distance from a main highway. Sometimes because the very nature of back-mountains was so rugged and defiant and unassailable that their inhabitants seemed to take on the qualities of the hills themselves. Buffalo Valley was such a place.

It was country with a character of its own. Rugged, leave-me-alone mountain backwoods. Some folks there loved good moonshine whiskey and Saturday night dances. Sometimes, that combustible combination exploded into shooting matches and sometimes they were fatal. Poor country, as far as most were concerned. The few prominent ranchers and big landowners who owned the valley land had money, but most were much inclined to keep it.

There were 11 school districts in this valley and scattered in the mountains around it. Little eight-graded schools – Yanush, Laura, Lone Prairie, Anderson Creek, Lone Elm. When kids graduated from the eighth grade, they had no place to go. Latimer County had only three high schools: Wilburton, Red Oak and, by now, Panola. All of them were on Highway 270, which ran east and west through the north central part of the county, impossibly out of reach of the children of Buffalo Valley. Twenty-five or so of the lucky kids would trickle over the county lines to bordering school districts that supported high schools.

When E.T. Dunlap took his election campaign for school superintendent into the valley, people would wait for him after he spoke and tell him how heartbreaking it was.

"We've wanted a high school over here for our children for years, but we've never been able to get anybody to help us."

After he took office as Latimer County's new superintendent of schools, the beautiful valley with no high school even in horseback range would not leave his mind. And walking to his office on cold winter days he would remember the bitter-black mornings in the saddle with the horse slipping and skidding on ice, rain freezing his gloved hand to the pommel. And he would think about the kids of Buffalo Valley.

10

A Gamblin' Ol' White Fella

Phoenix, Arizona! This time on a bus and wearing new shoes and a new suit of clothes.

On this walk down that dirt road from the Watts farm to the bus station in Eufaula, not only had the bare soles of Wade's feet not touched the road, the soles of his brand new shoes weren't touching it much either. Wade Watts, whose daddy missed being a slave by two years, was off to school to be an attorney at law.

Aspiring young black men could take courses at Phoenix Junior College, and if they did well, the way could be opened for them at other schools where they could learn the law. It had been a proud moment for Charlie and Miz Watts when Wade walked across that stage at Washington High School and got the diploma that said he was a high school graduate and ready to go further than any Watts had ever gone. And he was only 20 years old.

"Where do you think you are going to law school, boy? Negroes can't go no place but Langston."

The man in the Eufaula drug store had said it.

"They teach the law there?"

"Nope."

Kirksey had tried to help.

"Wade, the Legislature keeps a fund to help bright young Negroes who want to learn what they don't teach at Langston to go to college out of state."

Eagerly, Wade applied. Word came back. The legislative scholarship fund for Negroes had $8 in it. But, Miz Watts wasn't to be defeated. If this rambling boy of hers who couldn't keep a breakfast fire lit was willing to study the law and be somebody, she was willing to wash and iron white folks' clothes and scrimp up enough money to put with what Wade had saved and send him where a Negro boy could study the law. Wade entered Phoenix triumphantly. Vengefully reliving that shameful moment in the park. "Damn that kid, I got my own living to make."

Well, that big ol' dumb kid was going to be a lawyer. Help make the world according to Roscoe Dunjee. Proudly, he presented himself at Phoenix Junior College.

"Where did you finish high school, son?"

"Eufaula, Oklahoma, sir. Washington High School."

"How many credits did they give?"

"I don't know nothing bout no credits."

The registrar left for the telephone. The news came back with that gritty sound of hot dust rattling through a ruined cornpatch.

"You only have 14 credits, son. You must have 18 to enroll in Phoenix Junior College."

"Damn these white people..."

Wade said it walking away from Phoenix Junior College.

"Ever which way I turn, I gettin' a switchin'."

Buckeye, Arizona, was a little farming town just west of Phoenix on the road to California. Wade stopped off there. It was coming on cotton-picking season, and cottonpickers were in much demand,

and Wade Watts knew cottonpicking. He may never know any law, but nobody ever accused Wade Watts of not knowing cottonpicking.

There was an old white fellow lived there in Buckeye. He was a gambler. And he made his money from Negroes who poured in for the cotton picking. Wade had never stopped remembering the confident way that gambling man in the park had scooped up his last 35 cents almost before the dice stopped rolling. This old white fella dealt out the cards on his kitchen table and scooped up the money in the same sure way.

Throughout that fall, Wade picked cotton during the day and lost the money he made from it at the old white fella's kitchen table at night. He studied the old man, trying to see what he was doing. Luck, he began to figure, had little to do with it. He stole a deck of his cards and took them home and studied them as he had tried to study the law. Held them up to the light. But, no matter how hard he tried, he couldn't study out how the old man knew what Wade was holding in his hand almost before Wade did.

Along about Christmas, Wade wrote home for bus money. This time, he sent the letter to his mama. He did not tell her he had invested all his school money and his whole fall's cotton-picking money at the old man's kitchen table, and that he had learned nothing except that he couldn't even learn gambling. Couldn't study the law. Couldn't learn gambling. Cotton picking was over. Time to go home broke again. Face Charlie Watts.

The old white fella was sitting on the porch in a rope-bottomed chair, tilted back against the wall of the house.

"Giving it up, boy?"

"Yessir, Goin' home."

He looked the boy over. Picked at his teeth with a sliver of wood cut from the porch pole.

"Wade," he said, "you're too good a boy to lose your money like you do."

Wade brightened. ("Give that boy his money back, don't do him that way.")

"Now I ain't about to give you no money back, but I've got something to tell you."

And the old man looked off up the road and picked some more at his teeth.

"You'll be surprised to know that I've been had to cheat on you ever since you've been here."

"Nossir, I ain't surprised, but you so clever I never could catch you."

The front legs of the tilted chair slammed down on the boards of the porch.

"Fetch that tub over here, boy, and set down."

And the old man's deft hands flew over the cards, and he dealt Wade a hand that contained two kings. But he dealt himself two aces. Dealt Wade three aces. Gave himself a full house, deuces and treys. Shuffled. Cut. Dealt out a straight flush. Shuffled. Dealt out a royal straight flush.

It was the greatest wonder the boy had ever seen.

"Now, pay 'tention, boy."

And he showed Wade in great detail how to know what the second card down was and how to deal it out from under there without anybody seeing. How to know when somebody else was dealing seconds.

"Listen, you hear that?"

"Hear what?"

"Look off up the road there and listen."

And Wade heard it.

"Ssssp."

For the first time in his life, Wade could hear the cards talking to him.

"When you hear that ssssp, somebody is dealing seconds to you so fast you can't see they're dealing you seconds, but when you hear that, they are. You listen!"

"Ssssp."

"They don't do that coming off the top. Ssssp. Somebody dealing you seconds."

And class continued.

"When you stack a deck, you stack it in the deal. There are three people in the game. I'm going to make you my buddy hand and we gon bust this man over here. I'll give this man kings and I'll give you aces. And what I'll do, I put a king on top and an ace, and a king and another ace, and then put one card in between there. I'm doing all this in the shuffle. And then I whip 'em over, just like I'm really whipping them. And my buddy here cuts them, see. Looks like he cuts them, but he leaves them just like they are on the cut, and then this fella we gon bust gets kings and you get aces. Then I'm sitting here now, and I'm watching to see that the other fella don't hit. He's got kings, maybe there's a third king coming off. Then I knock second on him and give him that under card and give you that third king."

Sssp. It was the world's sweetest sound.

"And we bust im."

And it went on. How to deal off the bottom, how to run up the pot. How to mark the cards with a solution of alcohol and ink so secretly nobody in the world could ever see but you, even if they held them up to the light. The old white man taught the young black man the art of making a living cheating at cards. And when he was through he set the deck of cards neatly on the bottom of the upturned tub.

"Wade? How much money you figure you left on my kitchen table?"

"Season pickin'. Guess bout $500, on top a my school money."

The old white man tapped the deck of cards with his finger.

"I've just give you a thousand-dollar education. Now you go on away from here and you don't lose no more of your money like you been doing."

"Yessir, yessir, I won't do no more of that."

"And don't you come round here trying to take an old white man's money. Only cheatin' goin' on at my kitchen table is gonna be done by me."

❖

There are two ways to form a new high school. One is by consolidation of all the schools in the area, doing away with the elementary schools and building one central school for all 12 grades.

E.T. Dunlap explained all that to the people of Buffalo Valley who gathered into his new county superintendent's office in Wilburton. But it costs a lot of money and it kicks up a lot of dust from mamas who are easier with their younger children going to the little school just down the road. E.T. had called them in, the leaders of the 11 school districts of Buffalo Valley: school principals, teachers, board members, citizens.

"Or," he told them, "there is what is known as a union-graded school in which all of the districts are put into one administrative unit, a central school building built for the junior and senior high students, and the first six grades left close to home in their old elementary schools.

"The second method," he told them, "is more economically feasible because there are fewer central school buildings to construct immediately, and it is more politically palatable to leave the little children close to home."

Everybody began to get excited. And so did E.T.

"We would put on buses and haul them in," he said. "And listen to this: Within a short time, as big brother and big sister get on those nice, shiny school buses every morning to come down to this bright, shiny new schoolhouse where we have a lot going on – basketball, music programs – the younger kids are going to demand an opportunity to get on that bus and ride it down here. By the time they are ready to come, the parents will be ready to let them."

It was unanimous. Buffalo Valley wanted a high school. E.T. drew up petitions for each of the 11 school districts.

"It's going to cost money. Opposition will come. Take my word for it, opposition will come."

They hurried. E.T. gave them three days to circulate the petitions. Called the election at little Laura School in the middle of the district. Went over and conducted the election personally, made the ballots, set up a committee of watchers to keep it honest. And the people came in from the valley and the mountains that surrounded it, and they voted yes by nearly 80 per cent.

"Opposition will come," E.T. warned.

Moving fast, they elected a new central school board. A man who owned land near the center of the district donated ten acres. E.T. didn't pause. He scheduled an election to vote $5,000 in bonds to build the school building, the maximum that could be voted under the law.

Then opposition came.

Superintendents of schools across the county lines who had been seeping off a few kids from along the border didn't want to lose them. They agitated the well-to-do ranchers and big landholders of Buffalo Valley who didn't want to pay more taxes. Together, they hired a lawyer and made up a little money to oppose the bond issue. Before it was over, eight lawsuits had been filed to stop the $5,000 bond issue and prevent Buffalo Valley from having its own high school. One of them went all the way to the Oklahoma Supreme Court. But nobody thought to ask for temporary injunctions while the cases were being heard, and nobody in Buffalo Valley was waiting.

While the lawyers argued, E.T. and the folks of Buffalo Valley held the election and voted the bonds, and E.T. went to work on friendly congressmen and senators to get federal WPA funds for the building. But the Depression was losing its grip in the face of rumors that war was coming with much fear and many jobs. The Works Progress Administration that had built so many schools in Oklahoma was being phased out. But E.T. kept at them, the way old J.O. Rich had kept on at the state school officials about issuing one more third-grade teaching certificate. Told the federal officials about all those kids, and how it felt to ride a horse seven miles to school when the rain froze your glove to the saddlehorn.

"Where you goin', Pete?"

Wade, plodding the dust from home to town to buy himself a new pair of shoes and a decent suit of clothes to replace the raggedy cotton-picking clothes he had worn on the bus from Phoenix, met the old home boy at the edge of town.

"Buck and them got a poker game going, and they wants a new deck a cards."

Wade's hand shot into his pocket, fingered the two dollars and a half his mama had given him for new shoes. The five dollars for a new suit of clothes.

"I just walk along with you if it okay, Pete."

"Come on, but stay outta that game, Wade. Ol' Buck he's sho nuff hot today."

Hours later, Wade left the card game in the same old shoes, but the right-hand pocket of his raggedy old pants was swelled tight with $94 in the old home boys' money.

"Old white fella? You done been wrong about that thousand-dollar education. That ain't even goin' to be a beginnin'."

And the worn-out shoes scuffed pure happiness from the dying-rose-colored dust of the road.

part two

"I don't know this Stipe boy that is running against me," C. Plowboy Edwards would say when he was out talking with folks on the street. And he'd reach into his pocket and pull out that picture.

"But I think that's him, stomping that flag."

**1941** *A continent of Jewry was in flight; German troops destroyed Jewish shops, factories, department stores, libraries, synagogues, and cemeteries. German troops invaded Russia, advanced rapidly against the Soviet army which had been depleted of leadership by Josef Stalin's political purges. Germans machine-gunned 96,000 Ukrainians. People in besieged Leningrad ate cats, dogs, birds, jelly made of cosmetics, soup made from boiled leather wallets.*

President Roosevelt's third inaugural message called for freedom of speech and religion, freedom from want, and freedom from fear, anyway. Worldwide. The Great Depression was gone. Money was flowing so quickly into circulation in the United States, war bonds were issued to try to help reduce it.

Pearl Harbor is a beautiful, sunny inlet on the southern coast of Oahu, Hawaii. When the United States annexed Hawaii in 1900, we put a U.S. Naval base there as an outpost to keep us safe. On a quiet Sunday morning of that December, Japanese planes attacked it, sinking the battleships Arizona, Oklahoma, California, Nevada, and West Virginia, destroying 200 U.S. planes. Killing 2,344 American men.

The United States declared war on Japan. Germany, Italy, Romania and Bulgaria declared war on the United States. The storm finally had broken. Directly overhead.

11

Pearl

"Wade? You in there?"

"Yeah."

"You outta bed?"

"No, come on in. Mama and Daddy and the kids at church."

It was that Sunday in December of 1941 in Eufaula, Oklahoma. Wade had played cards late the night before and slept away the day. His friend, Billy Ray, still was drinking, and he had brought some by for Wade. He sat down beside the bed.

"You hear about Pearl Harbor?"

"Who she?"

"Ain't no woman, Wade. You don't know nothing about Pearl Harbor?"

"No."

"Well, let me put it like this. You been looking for a job, and we done found you one."

"Doin' what?"

"We gon give you a dollar a day for dodging bullets and the first one you miss dodging, you lose your job."

❖

Hayden Hackney Donahue knew instantly that Pearl Harbor was no woman. Donahue was born in El Reno in 1912, and spent part of his boyhood in a little town about ten miles south of Peaceable Mountain. His dad never was put in prison for union activities, but he had been fired for trying to organize employees of the Rock Island Railroad in El Reno. That firing was what had brought the family to Pittsburg, a town owned by McAlester Fuel Company, which operated three coal mines and a company store. Hayden's dad became an administrator of one of the mines, and for his work he was paid in company scrip usable at the company store. Baby things were sold in the front, children's stuff in the middle, adult stuff at the back, and, in the far back, was a funeral parlor.

Hayden hadn't been a farm kid like Joe and Wade and Elijah Thomas. He had lived in town, but the family could keep a cow and some chickens, and local fields were available for roaming. By the middle 1920s,

Hayden Hackney Donahue, on his way to the bloody battlefields of North Africa.

about the time Eugene Earl was born to J.I. and Eva Lucinda on Peaceable Mountain, coal mining in Oklahoma had begun to decline, and the Donahue family ended up in Sioux City, Iowa. So, although they were raised only about ten miles apart they never got a chance to run across each other. The Great Crash of 1929 wiped out the last of the Donahue money and an uncle gave Hayden money to enter Kansas University at Lawrence in 1930, the year Karl Menninger, psychiatrist at the famous Menninger Clinic at nearby Topeka, published *The Human Mind*, explaining that psychiatry is a legitimate and relatively uncomplicated source of help for mentally disturbed persons. Menninger wrote the text for medical students, but the book was a hit with the public. It didn't impress Hayden Donahue. He had chosen engineering for his short-term goal of getting enough to eat and pre-medical school for his long-time goal of becoming what he wanted to be.

About the time Joe's leg went bad and Wade hopped his first freight train for California, Hayden was working for Roosevelt's Public Works Administration and the State of Kansas surveying and designing lakes and making topographical maps and longing to go to medical school.

By that bright Sunday morning in December of 1941, Donahue was a nice young man trying to study bone surgery at the University of Georgia. But, he kept getting sidetracked into other things, like polio epidemics and pneumonia outbreaks that required out of compassion that he practice what he already knew rather than press on to what he wanted to be. And, there was psychiatry. Everywhere he turned, he found that infant profession had planted itself squarely in front of him and would not let him around.

When he was studying to be a doctor at the University of Kansas, he had attended a lecture by Dr. Menninger, and the "egos" and "ids" and other stangenesses that he heard turned him decisively toward something that made more sense, like bone surgery. And he had made up his mind once and for all about that. He thought.

Then he accepted an internship at Georgia, and found himself working alongside a man named Hervey Cleckley. And, of course, Hervey Cleckley was no bone surgeon. He was a gifted psychiatrist trying to set up a department of psychiatry at Georgia, and he thought Hayden Donahue had been born for psychiatry. Donahue and Cleckley had bonded over one of the earliest versions of the electroshock machine. Here is how Donahue would recall it:

> Cleckley ordered the machine, and when it arrived we told our first patient, a 45-year-old chronically depressed man, what we had in mind. We said we didn't know how it worked, but that some patients had obtained good therapeutic benefits. He was agreeable, so we took out the manual and determined where to place the electrodes, and the prescribed voltage. Then I pushed the button. And this guy like to flew off the table. It scared both Cleckley and me. Next time, we got four aides to hold the patient down.

And the craziest thing of all was that once the electroshock had, in effect, gotten the patient's attention, Donahue had found he could sit down with him and quickly uncover the painful emotional burr causing the man's hidden anxieties, and then true healing could start. Sure as a knitting bone. Donahue finally had agreed to become the first psychiatry resident in the first psychiatry department at the University of Georgia. But, that's the point at which the Japanese bombs got at their slaughter, and the U.S. needed doctors, and Hayden Hackney Donahue's forever-budding career was off on another crazy carom.

War arrived in McAlester in the form of jobs. United States troops were needing places to store German prisoners of war. Fifteen-year-old Joe Stipe read an ad in the newspaper seeking men for "fine grading" at a prisoner-of-war camp being built on the northeast edge of town. Fifty cents an hour. When Joe showed up, they handed him a shovel. The consummate tool, they grinned, for fine grading. Within three days, he was transferred to the southwest of McAlester to an eleven-square-mile anthill of activity. The new Naval Ammunition Depot would manufacture the ammunition necessary for the war. Joe helped unload the first car of lumber onto the field.

"There's going to be all the work a man can do for as long as he wants to work there, Dad," he told J.I. "Fifty cents an hour."

"Well," said J.I., "I have made more money than that."

And he grinned at his son.

"But not lately."

Joe transferred to the swing shift in the fall so he could work through his last year in high school.

❖

That following summer, Latimer County's superintendent of schools, E.T. Dunlap, roomed at Oklahoma A&M College at Stillwater and worked on his master's degree. His master's thesis was on the formation of the new Buffalo Valley School District. He was writing autobiography, so it wasn't all that difficult. His roommate was the superintendent of schools at Jay, and he also was a member of the State Board of Education. He offered E.T. a job as high school inspector for the State Department of Education. E.T. decided he would resign as county superintendent of schools and accept it as soon as he had the kinks worked out of the new school he had launched. Everything finally was ready to go. Almost.

By September, 1942, Buffalo Valley High School had become the last school building in Oklahoma to be constructed with WPA federal bonds, just as the man who built it had become the last teacher certified by the old teacher examination system. All the lawsuits had been settled in favor of the new high school, E.T. had gotten his degree, won re-election as county superintendent without opposition and ceased going into Buffalo Valley after dark until some of the anger of the opponents died down. But, it was done.

The school board was in place, the faculty was hired, the bright new buses bought, the equipment installed, courses of study prepared, a student body of 150 enrolled and ready to learn. But the school had no superintendent. Many schoolmen had gone off to war, and those who did not go were not eager to go into the kind of war they were having in Buffalo Valley. Everybody scrambled to find a qualified school superintendent who would take the job. Couldn't. None was available.

As E.T. said it to John Prock in that way of his, "The opposition to the school has helped to generate some undesirability on the part of school men of going over there and taking that new superintendency."

Finally, on Sept. 1, 1942, E.T. called together the Latimer County commissioners and resigned as county superintendent of schools, but he didn't become a high school inspector. He called Buffalo Valley High School and took the job as superintendent. He opened his own school on schedule. After a month, he found a superintendent willing to come, and he resigned and went on to the State Department of Education. But he kept his eye on his school. Visited. Tried to help the new guy blaze the first trail through new country. But, by mid-year, the superintendent quit. It was just too tough. E.T. went back to Red Oak, and hired Presley Askew, principal of Red Oak School and a well-known basketball coach. Presley saw the new high school through the remainder of its first year, and then he wanted no more of Buffalo Valley.

E.T. had a "little" brother named Leo, who was three years younger than E.T., but he was six-feet-four and weighed about 250 pounds. He had become principal of Red Oak School when Presley Askew left it for the superintendency at Buffalo Valley. Leo had watched his older brother struggle with Buffalo Valley. Finally, he couldn't stand it.

"I'll take that job on," he said, "and I'll stay with it and make it go."

"Listen, little brother…"

And E.T. explained it to him.

"The people over there in that Buffalo Valley country are tough, brother. Some of them are mean. They've run off two superintendents during the first year. Now, if you want to take them on, that's what you will be getting into."

Leo grinned in that way E.T. could remember from when they were kids on the ranch.

"I'll take them on," he said.

And he did.

E.T. took him over and introduced him to the board and they offered him the job of Buffalo Valley Superintendent of Schools, and he accepted it, and E.T. went on back to his job as a state high school inspector. First thing Leo got for his new job was a deputy's commission from the county sheriff, and when he went to a basketball game or to a meeting he carried a pistol on his hip. Let the folks know he would put the pistol aside if they wished and take them on in a fist fight if they wanted that. And he got along with the folks of Buffalo Valley, even those who wanted no school there at all. Leo Dunlap developed a school. And, as E.T. predicted, the little children left scattered out in the little districts soon were clamoring to come to the big main school and be a part of the things their big brothers and sisters came home talking about – the basketball and the physical education and the special music programs, and dramatics and the school plays. But, mostly, they wanted to ride those shiny new school buses that left their front doors every week-day morning with their big brothers and sisters aboard. The district built a big central elementary school. Opposition trickled to nothing. Leo stayed 16 years and developed one of the finest consolidated school systems in the eastern part of Oklahoma before the state superintendent finally hired him away to work in the State Department of Education.

❖

There is, among card players, a kind of honor system designed to save those who have the presence of mind to wish to avert total financial tragedy. Under that system, the money a man puts on the table is fair game, and the card sharps get it any way they can. When they cheat, you have to learn to cheat better. Really good cheaters love to come across a better cheater, considering it a matter of self improvement. They learn how he is cheating and add his skill at it to their own. Cheaters are known in their own circles as players. Non-cheaters are known as suckers.

All agree that the money a man keeps in his pocket may be for some sacred thing such as to pay his rent or buy groceries or take the baby to the doctor or for Saturday night whiskey, and so long as he does not touch it, it is not considered a part of the game. It is not politically correct to try to force him into his pocket, no matter how bad it frustrates a player with a fat-pocketed sucker. But there are participants, almost always the suckers, who disrespect that honor system. They are looked down on most of all. They sneak table money into their pocket when they are winning and then sneak it back onto the table in support of a winning hand – a special kind of cheating that makes a good player mad. That is what this big white guy sitting across from Wade in Ada was doing. No doubt about it. But he was big, and white, and dangerous. So Wade kept quiet and watched him some more.

Sure enough. Good hand. He fumbled in his shirt pocket as if for a cigarette and took money out and eased it onto the table. So-so hand, he would take it up and ease it back into his shirt pocket. Wade dealt the man two kings. Watched the fingers go to the pocket. Wade dealt himself two aces. The pile of money in the middle of the table grew as the betting went around the table. The man looked at his hand again, looked uneasily at Wade and bet the three dollars and a half that lay on the table in front of him. Wade threw out a twenty-dollar bill.

"Raise you the other $16.50."

"I ain't got it."

"Yeah, you do. You got money in your pocket up there."

The man's eyes turned mean.

"It ain't poker to make a man play money out of his pocket."

"Yeah, I knew that when you was playing money out of your pocket before, but if you want to see this hand, you gon have to call that $16.50."

The man exploded across the table, towering over Wade with his fists tight, wedging him helpless into the chair so he couldn't get up.

"Man, go ahead and take the money."

Wade said it softly.

"Take the twenty and all. It's alright."

In addition to what the old white fellow in Phoenix had taught him, Wade was a good natural card player. He could remember things. Who he dealt an ace to, who smiled almost imperceptibly when someone else dealt them one, an old three-legged chair with a broken seat kicked against the wall behind him. Which three legs remained. Their looseness in the old sockets. The distance. The necessary time.

The big white man sat back down, muttering about out-of-town niggers. The instant the man's eyes went back to his cards, Wade moved. The near leg came loose easily. Became a nightstick in his hand. He slammed it across the man's head, and the man went down. Wade carefully picked his twenty from amid the man's money that had scattered on the table, and the game went on. With one less player.

12

The Man with the Little Old Hide House

When Wade reported for the draft, they told him he was physically unfit for the Army, and he didn't ask them why. He moved to Ada where he had been gambling off and on. Lots of white folks with money sat in on the games, and Wade liked that. He did not like to play cards with Negroes. They didn't have much money to start with, and they were squabbly when they lost it. He met a girl, got to thinking about getting married, and started hunting honest work for the daytime.

There was a man who had a little old hide house there in Ada where they sold cattle hides. The man bought the hides in bulk from the slaughterhouse and resold them. Somebody told Wade he might get a steady job there. He didn't, but he got to meet the man who owned it. He was a big man. Forceful. With twinkling eyes and a sharp wit. Words rolled out of his mouth smooth and round like Kirksey's. Took him five minutes to unfold up out of a chair. And, he was a lawyer. The fella that run the hide house for him introduced them.

"This," he said, "is Robert S. Kerr. He owns the place. And he is going to be the next governor of Oklahoma."

❖

Historically, two election campaigns were conducted for each office in Oklahoma. One was for white folks, the other for the Negroes. Negroes usually did not attend white election gatherings. If they did they stayed in the back where they could not be seen or heard. But the Negroes had managed to hang on to their vote, and the white candidates needed it. And they needed a method of getting it without risking loss of any white votes. So, they appointed two campaign managers, a white man to handle the white folks and a Negro to campaign the blacks. No white candidate dared promise anything special to the blacks, even when speaking in "nigger town," for fear that word of it would leak into the white community and defeat them. Negro campaign workers were sometimes rewarded with what was called "nigger jobs," usually janitorial or dealing with an all-black institution. Precedent for this had been established by William Henry David Murray back in 1906 when he was elected president of the Constitutional Convention. He had been appalled to find that the territorial legislature had hired Negroes as clerks when white men were doing janitor work. So, Alfalfa Bill had asked the convention for authority to do the hiring and the firing. He fired all the Negroes from the clerical jobs and all the whites from the janitorial jobs. Then he hired them back and reversed the roles.

Negro voters did not particularly want their white candidates to promise them anything directly because anybody with judgement that bad probably couldn't win, anyway. They listened closely to the white candidates' speeches, however, for terms like common people, working folks, and the poor, hoping for some promise that would trickle down to them when the white folks were done with it.

When Kirksey Nix had run for the state House of Representatives in Eufaula back in '38, Wade had worked the

Negro community for him. Although he had been only 19 and couldn't vote, he had made talks for Kirksey every time he could get a crowd together and even talked on the radio for him once. And Kirksey had carried the Negro community strong. Since then, when the loud speakers started pulsing and the flags started waving and the bands started playing, Wade would get a kind of an itch in his system. Like he got when he saw some sharpie riffling a new deck of cards.

When Robert S. Kerr filed as a candidate for governor of Oklahoma, Wade got himself a loud speaker and mounted it on his old pickup and threw a mattress in the back. He went to the Negro who was managing the black campaign for Mr. Kerr in Ada and cut himself a deal. Mr. Kerr would buy gasoline for the truck, and buy Wade some food when he was on the road campaigning, and, who knows, there might be a job he could do for some money after Kerr was elected governor.

Wade kept a close eye on the Negro community. Anytime they scheduled a speaking, he would tell the Kerr campaign about it. Politicians had to pay to get time at a public speaking. The Kerr campaign seemed happy to give him the $50 to buy time on the platform and then get up and tell the Negroes why Bob Kerr was the best candidate to be the white folks' governor. Wade spotted it for a scam right off. The people who organized the public speakings got off with most of the money that was paid, but it was a good, clean scam and it was the way things were done in Oklahoma in 1942. Wade was careful never to ask for money for himself, because he didn't want to damage his chances of getting that job when the campaign was over.

He worked the little Negro towns and the black sides of the white towns, getting up at daybreak to put up signs. Evenings when people got off work, he'd start that P.A. system to playing some religious music he knew Negroes liked. Maybe 15 or 20 people would gang around for the music, and Wade would tell

*Joe Stipe, wearing straw hat, and his brother, Jack, in Navy uniform.
At right is friend, Sammy Marlow.*

them they should vote for Robert S. Kerr. Speak 15 or 20 minutes, and trail the gospel music off out of that town and to the
next one. Sometimes, he could make two or three little towns in
one night. When the last prospective voter had gone to bed,
Wade would crawl into the back of the pickup and get him some
sleep on the old mattress. Thinking, as he drifted to sleep under
the stars, about this job he wanted.

Robert S. Kerr defeated Gomer Smith and a field of lesser Democratic lights in the primary election of 1942 and defeated a Republican with an unpronounceable name to become Oklahoma's twelfth governor on Jan. 13, 1943. First native-born. Wade shrugged and told his new wife:

"Way I understand it, they got jobs that they call nigger jobs, and they got jobs they call white man's jobs. And I guess that job I wanted was a white man's job why I didn't get it."

❖

"Dear Joe:

"The Navy is wonderful. Three meals every day and a good place to sleep. The work isn't much compared to chopping cotton and hoeing corn on Peaceable Mountain."

Joe Stipe was too mature to worry any more about the hants that hung around the old abandoned house that separated his house from the mailbox where he walked to get the letters from his older brother, Jack. But the letters tortured him. Everybody from Pittsburg County had gone to war except for Joe and Eugene

Crowell whose harelip kept him out of military service. Joe had completed two years of school in one and graduated from high school at 16, so he was too young to go to war. It embarrassed him to walk down the street when everybody he knew was somewhere else in the world fighting a war to make America safe. The whole world was in upheaval, rolling and tumbling, and the sound of thunder was everywhere. Jack was off on a ship somewhere, another of the clan gone from Peaceable Mountain. And with each of their going the old house had grown quieter. Not only had Jack gone off to war, but all of his friends had gone with him, and all of Joe's friends had followed close behind. Except for Eugene Crowell.

"That," Jack quipped in a letter, "is what you get for memorizing the *Book of Knowledge* and graduating early."

When Joe couldn't stand it any longer, he and Eugene hitchhiked to California to work in the shipyards. Joe celebrated his 17th birthday in October of 1943 in the Navy recruiting office in San Diego, California, being sworn into the Navy by a ruggedly handsome recruiting captain named William Bendix. J.I. married a lady named Rosie Stiles and acquired a stepdaughter, Pauline, and moved off Peaceable Mountain and into town.

On the brutal, mind-butchering battlefields of South Africa, Hayden Hackney Donahue, flight surgeon, was making the final, gut-level shift from physician to psychiatrist. He saw psychiatry work there amid the slaughter. His commanding officer was psychiatrist-neurologist Roy Grinker, a master who had studied with Sigmund Freud and had set up the University of Chicago's psychiatry department. Talk of the ego and the id no longer unsettled the young doctor's mind.

Grinker was blazing new trails in combat psychiatry. In the past, soldiers suffering from shell shock and combat fatigue had been withdrawn far from the bloody thunder of battle for treatment. Grinker said pulling them away offered only a temporary cure, and he wanted them healed. His idea was to keep the men in treatment centers close to combat and treat them – now using sodium Pentothal instead of electroshock – not in a luxury hotel, but within hearing of the artillery, the same environment that had traumatized them. It had to be done fast. There was no time for standard psychoanalytical work. The soldiers could not be put on the couch for a year.

Donahue learned two valuable lessons there on the battlefields of Africa. One was that mental patients treated in places removed from what had made them sick, but not too far removed, had a far better chance of recovery than those who were isolated from the reality of it. Donahue watched Grinker win this argument with the military. Saw him prove the validity of his theory in field hospitals placed halfway between the death zone and the safety of the rear lines, safe enough to permit recovery, but not so removed from reality they could not go back. Donahue began to look less at the care of individual patients and more at development of a modern, enlightened system in which any good psychiatrist could do his healing.

Grinker convinced the military so thoroughly, they began to look around for more psychiatrists. There was none. And that was where Donahue learned his second major lesson: when psychiatrists are unavailable, medical doctors can be interested, taught, and brought into the battle against mental illness. The idea belonged to Grinker. The Army bought it. Donahue remembered it.

Grinker was given a resort hotel on the beach in St. Petersburg, Fla., for a training facility and hospital and ordered to develop and run a three-month training program in psychiatry for physicians in other specialties. He took with him his most promising young understudy. Hayden Donahue was named director of professional services.

13

World War II Ends in Mississippi

On April 25, 1945, patrols from the Russian and U.S. armies met on the Elbe River just south of Berlin, signaling completion of a sweep of Allied troops through Germany. Far into the night, they toasted the end of the war in Europe with whiskey, vodka, and accordion music.

On May 7, in Reims, France, the champagne country to the east-northeast of Paris – on ground once trod by Joan of Arc – the German Commander in Chief signed an unconditional surrender to representatives of America, Britain, France and Russia. And at Millsap College in Jacksonville, Mississippi, the special students in the U.S. Navy's V-5 section got drunk and celebrated the war they never got to attend.

Because of exceptional talents and intelligence, they had been vented from the stream of American youth enroute to the battle fields and sent to Millsap where they had struggled with flight instruction, calculus and analytical geometry and played football and poker with other bright young white men like Johnny Carson and Hilary

Hinton Ziglar, known then and later when he became famous as Zig. A brilliant kid named Bob Bates from Seminole, Oklahoma, was there. And a kid from Peaceable Mountain named Joe.

Joe had known from the moment he got there that he was in trouble. These guys knew calculus, analytical geometry, physics from the advanced high schools they had attended. Savanna High School had offered one course in algebra. Many nights when the other guys were playing poker or sleeping, Joe was hitting the books. But, then, before they even began to prepare Joe to help Jack save the world for democracy, the war began to wear down, and they started phasing out the Naval unit at Millsap, sending all the bright young men out to colleges around the country where they could play football and become engineers, scientists, anything their young and vigorous minds lusted after.

There was an old Navy chief at Millsap who had taken a liking to Joe, and Joe had taken a liking to him. In civilian life a writer for the New Orleans Picayune, the chief was a salty old fellow in peace or in war. It was natural that he and Joe would celebrate victory together. But the celebration of victory in Europe went on well past tolerable limits in Jacksonville, Mississippi. The executive officer decided to begin court-martial proceedings against the tardy young revelers for being absent without leave – until the old chief got back and informed the executive officer that he had been in command of the revelry. The commanding officer called to say he thought the court-martial was not a good idea, either. He had, he said, stopped by the party for a few drinks himself.

Joe was more than six feet tall and permanently tough from growing up on Peaceable Mountain, hoeing corn and chopping cotton and sawing all that firewood. The old chief thought he was destined for football greatness. When they started breaking up the V-5 school and sending the midshipmen off to other colleges, he wanted his alma mater, Tulane, to derive the benefits of Joe's tackling and blocking skills in its football frontline – and the chief could follow his progress to stardom. So an intricate military political deal was cut to get Joe assigned to Tulane.

There was a good running back at Millsap named Schultz, and there was another officer whose alma mater was the University of South Carolina. He participated in the chief's deal on the condition that Schultz be sent to his alma mater. And so, neither sailor approached the re-assignments sheet on the bulletin board with any anxiety. Each knew where he was going.

But there are within large organizations filled with powerful people some little people with no apparent power at all who can divert even the most awesome power. Somewhere in the massive bureaucracy that was the Navy, a clerk thought it would be fun if Schultz went to Tulane and Joe Stipe went to South Carolina. So when Joe and Schultz strolled up to the bulletin board they found neither was going where he thought he was going. The old chief was so furious he went all the way to his congressman seeking redress, but it didn't work. Congress didn't honor political deals other than its own. Besides, in the U.S. Navy, the paperwork is more incomprehensible in its majesty than even the Congress of the United States of America. When orders are cut, they are circulated throughout the Bureau of Naval Personnel, various commands and the post where the sailor is going. Hundreds of copies ooze like lava in all directions throughout the bureaucracy. Supply section gets a copy. The paymaster. And, like harsh words, once they are out, there is no getting them back. The running back went to Tulane. Joe went to the University of South Carolina at Columbia and played football and got his degree in general engineering in a rigid academic regimen of six trimesters – 120 hours – in two years. And tutored the running back they were left with in order to keep him in school long enough for a winning football season.

For three and a half years, Elijah Thomas Dunlap, in the employ of the Department of Education, had toured the high schools of Oklahoma checking them for accreditation. The state was divided into four districts with a high school inspector for each district, and the inspectors would routinely trade districts from time to time. E.T. had come to know about every high school in Oklahoma, and he noticed something disturbingly familiar: the state had 4,451 school districts, but there were only about 600 high schools. Hundreds of elementary students had no access to high schools. It was Buffalo Valley on a statewide scale. In July of 1945, he could take it no more. He quit his job and went back to Latimer County, this time as superintendent of schools in Red Oak, getting on home ground for what he was about to do.

Red Oak was a small school district of about eight square miles, as it had been when he went to school there. Within 45 days E.T. put together 13 school districts and formed the biggest school district in Eastern Oklahoma. It covered 258 square miles. Little kids could stay close to home in their elementary schools. Shiny new school buses hauled their big brothers and sisters to the big high school that would gradually become the dream of the youngsters who couldn't yet go.

E.T. built Red Oak into the first North Central accredited high school in that part of the state other than in McAlester. He launched his quest for a doctor's degree by attending classes during the summer at Oklahoma A&M. Buffalo Valley was still on his mind, the way things were so different down there now in the beautiful remote country deep in the old Choctaw Nation country with its rugged leave-me-alone mountain character. It was now the going thing for young men and women straight out of the hills to go on to high school, play basketball, participate in the music program, act in the school plays. And more and more Buffalo Valley kids were showing up well prepared at the colleges and universities, especially at Wilburton's Eastern Oklahoma A&M. Then E.T. dropped his bombshell.

"I want," he announced to John Prock, "to try to reorganize the whole State of Oklahoma – to achieve the objective of every student in the state living in the atmosphere of a 12-graded school district."

He wanted every graduating elementary student to have a school bus waiting for them to haul them to high school. In 1946, he filed as a candidate for the Oklahoma House of Representatives. Buffalo Valley voted for him by almost 90 per cent.

Lucas Finney was an old white fella. A short man, chunky, with thinning gray hair. He was more of a sucker than a player when it came to cards, but he knew a player when he saw one. He ran a grocery store in Ada. Wade sat in on a gambling game with him one night, dealing seconds, sssp, off the bottom, stacking hands so smoothly that nobody ever guessed. Wade beat the old white fella out of $800, and he thought with a chuckle about all the school and cotton-picking money left on the kitchen table in Buckeye, Arizona. An old white fella taketh, another old white fella giveth back. Lucas Finney sat there studying Wade after the game ended. Then he borrowed $200 of his money back.

"You come over to the store in the morning, son, and I'll give you your $200."

Wade showed up early, and Mr. Finney handed him his $200.

"Another game tonight, Mr. Finney?"

"No, Wade, I can't match you. But, now, if you would be fair, I could fix it so you could really make some money."

"Fair?"

Wade's eyes flashed. The old white fella met his look.

"Square with me."

"What you talking about?"

Old Lucas Finney was on dangerous ground.

A war-weary and peace-hungry world sat up and looked around. The preceding year, 1945, had been one of historic endings. The first atomic bomb had been dropped on the Japanese city of Hiroshima, ending the World War. United States President Franklin Delano Roosevelt had died of a cerebral hemorrhage at Warm Springs, Georgia. He had brought the world's greatest experiment in freedom back from the brink of disaster. Adolph Hitler had killed himself in a bunker in Berlin. His program of hate had resulted in slaughter of 14 million non-combatants and wrecked half the civilized world.

The new year opened with hope – and caution. With the help of powerful Oklahoma senator Elmer Thomas, Governor Robert S. Kerr persuaded Congress to authorize the Arkansas River Navigation project to bring shipping up from the Gulf of Mexico to Tulsa. The first session of the U.N. General Assembly convened in London. The U.S. Army Signal Corps made radar contact with the moon. Work was completed on the first electronic computer. It filled a room. England's Winston Churchill announced to the world that an Iron Curtain had been dropped across Europe by America's war ally, Russia. The world's first ball-point pens went on the market, worrying bankers that such casual signatures might not be legal. A Frenchman named Louis Réard introduced the world's scantiest two-piece bathing suit. It was called the bikini.

14

Lonely Is the Sheepherder

The first thing Joe Stipe and Bob Bates saw in Rock Springs, Wyoming, was the whorehouse. Before, even, they saw the mines. Being full grown men now and veterans of the Great War they decided it was time to do their masculine duty at the whorehouse as well as in the mines. And then they would have that and coal mining out of the way and they could get on with their lives, better men for the experience of it.

After training at Millsap and college at the University of South Carolina, both young midshipmen had been given the option of becoming career officers in the Navy or taking a discharge. It was no longer heroic to be in the military, so both chose discharge. In June of 1946, they became ex-servicemen. Bob Bates' being from Seminole was what had first brought him and Joe together, but then they discovered there was more than that. Bob Bates was a debater. Certified best in the country. And he was brilliant. Best mind of anybody Joe had ever known. Joe and Bob had cemented their friendship at the National Forensic League Tournament in Charlotte, N.C. Joe's team had been beat in the quarter finals, and Joe was on his way back to the barracks when Bob scrambled to get Joe named official manager of the winning team so he could finish out his leave time in Charlotte and draw per diem as long as Bob kept winning. And Bob had kept winning until he was national champion. After their discharges, Bob had gone home to Seminole and Joe had gone home to McAlester.

J.I., living in town with his new wife, had gone to work for a power company digging holes for telephone poles. Joe had tried to find old black Dr. Wickham to tell him the Navy had never even questioned him about his bad leg. He wanted to ask about the yeast and the electrical device, and to see if he had ever figured out what had gone wrong with his leg. And to thank him as a man. But Dr. Wickham's widow, Pearl, told him the doctor had died the week before Joe came home.

Joe had grown up wanting to experience the coal-mining legends his dad once had brought home with his meager paycheck to the farmhouse on Peaceable Mountain. But Oklahoma mines were working mostly in the winter and then for low pay. Then Joe had read an ad in the newspaper that said miners were wanted in Rock Springs, Wyoming, to dig coal to fire the steam engines of the Union Pacific Railroad. And in Rock Springs, Wyoming, they were paying $16 a day. Joe called Bob Bates in Seminole.

They had decided to go by Detroit on their way to Wyoming and buy a new car since none was available in Oklahoma. New cars were to Detroit what coal once had been to McAlester, and if new cars were to be had, it would be in Detroit. They still had their Navy uniforms and their Navy pay, and the world still was full of gratitude for everything everybody had done to help win the war. Two young men in the dress whites of the Navy didn't wait long for rides on highways. They had hitch-hiked to Tinker Air Force Base in Oklahoma City where veterans could ride free on military aircraft if they happened to be going where the plane was going. The closest flight they had been able to get to Detroit before their patience ran out was to Scott Field, near Chicago. They had taken it, but the only cars for sale in Chicago were used taxis on which the speedometers had flipped more times than some cars had miles on them. The lure of the coal fields and $16 a day had pulled them west, hitch-hiking the highway. They had stopped off to work as barkers with a carnival until it was time to take the tents down, and the work had turned hard, and the pay had turned low, and it had become apparent baths would be few. They had quit and hit the highway again for Wyoming.

The old miners in Rock Springs laughed at them. Still in their Navy dress whites.

"You kids won't last a week."

The boys didn't know why the miners kept laughing until they got down into the mines. They found no legends there. Only hard, dirty work and irritable old men. Interminable hour after interminable hour. At the end of their first day, the boys walked unseeing past the whorehouse. Straight to a meal and a shower and a bed. Alone and grateful for it. Work got no easier. It was a week before they thought of anything except that shower, that quick dinner and that bed, where the muscles of their backs and shoulders continued to dig coal long after their minds were sound asleep. Finally, they decided to make a call at the whorehouse. And the old men laughed at them again.

The old white fella Lucas Finney ran a gambling game in the back of his grocery store after closing. All the gamblers around Ada, the suckers and the players, wound up there sooner or later. He and Wade decided on a 50-50 split of the profits with Mr. Finney getting all the glory. And the heat. Wade never would deal himself the winning hand, he would give it to Mr. Finney and let him beat the next fella. And when the game was over, Wade and everybody else at the table were losers. Except Mr. Finney. When they met later, Mr. Finney always split the money fair. They refined their partnership. Wade, circulating through the black community, would see a Negro with money to spend.

"I know where an old white boy lives over here, and me and you can go over there and bust 'im."

And they would go over and at night's end, Wade would be broke and his new friend would be broke and Mr. Finney would wind up with all the money. Wade and his newfound friend would console each other, and Wade would go by the store the next morning and get his split. He kept trying to get Mr. Finney to go after more white people.

"Number one," he would argue, "white folks got all the money.

"Number two, Negroes just ain't got that much to lose."

Number three, he couldn't tell even Mr. Finney. It was that special feeling he got in his fingers when he sent an educated white man home broke.

Mr. Finney was a racial segregationist, but he exempted Wade. It infuriated Mr. Finney when they went to a ballgame or somewhere and somebody tried to turn Wade away. They worked that out, too, with some help from Miz Watts' modicum of Indian blood.

"I'm sorry sir."

The ticket taker would always say it to Mr. Finney, never to Wade.

"No Negroes allowed in here."

"Negroes?"

Mr. Finney would raise his bushy gray eyebrows in surprise and look around.

"Where's any Negroes?"

And the ticket taker would dip his head awkwardly at Wade.

"Oh, him? That's no Negro, that's an Indian. Come on in here, Chief."

Nobody ever challenged Mr. Finney.

A pretty young girl seated Joe and Bob in the reception room of the Rock Springs whorehouse. The boys were invited to buy some drinks for the girls while they all kind of flirted and the girls showed off what they had to offer, the boys steadied their nerves, and were told as genteelly as possible that the girls had a schedule that was not negotiable. Three dollars for 15 minutes. Five dollars for thirty minutes. For $15 – a whole day of agony down in those mines – you could stay all night. During the second round of drinks, the girls began to get a little impatient with the boys. And during the third, there was a ruckus.

An old man in sheepskin coat, long white beard and an otherwise embarrassing state of indecency was chasing one of the girls down the stairs, swearing at every jump. He was followed by a woman in a maid's uniform who was screaming at every jump. When the old madam emerged from her room and settled everything down, it was learned that the maid had rung the three-dollar bell and the girl had jumped from under the old man as she had been trained to do.

The madam's eyes turned on the old sheepherder, and they turned mean.

"You are a cheap old son of a bitch," she said. "Spending all winter up there with them sheep and then coming in here …. If you'd a paid $5 there wouldn't be all this trouble."

And the old man was out in the street without his $3 or what he had paid it for. The necessities for his return to decency sailed out the door behind him.

"Joe?"

"Yeah, Bob."

"It's getting awful late."

"Maybe we better come back tomorrow night."

Neither slept until quite late.

"Joe?"

"Yeah, Bob."

"Maybe we ought to just get on to law school."

15

Surplus Sales and Backward Screws

The Servicemen's Readjustment Act, or G.I. Bill of Rights, voted by Congress while the war still was on, promised to pay for college education and to provide a low-interest home loan for any American men who managed to come out alive. Young veterans storming home with money for suburban homes set off a building boom and mass exodus from U.S. cities. More than two million suddenly crowded into the nation's classrooms. The University of Oklahoma campus was over-run. Housing in Norman became critical.

OU President Dr. George Cross purchased 500 tiny, square, prefabricated houses and erected them on campus south of Lindsey Street. The sudden settlement was called Sooner City, and a strong fire department became a necessity. Jack got a job there and helped Joe get on. It was a coveted job. Joe worked 12 hours and had 12 hours off, and got one weekend off a month. By juggling hours, he got a place to eat and sleep and study, and got paid for living there – with occasional interruptions to run somewhere and put out a fire. And any other work he could get his hands on.

Joe started hitting all the Army surplus sales. Buying stuff cheap and trying to sell it higher. He and Jack chipped in and bought an old surplus jeep for $200, and it became business vehicle and family car. The screws were probably the best deal Joe ever got on surplus. Or at least it so appeared.

Tons of screws. Sold them in bulk. Cheapest Joe had ever seen. He told Jack there was bound to be money in screws. Everybody used screws. So he kept bidding until he got so many of them it took a month to haul them away in the jeep. He hit on the idea of just grabbing up a handful of them, dropping them in a cellophane package and offering them as assorted screws. They didn't sell. He tried to wholesale them to hardware stores. Didn't sell. Cut his prices. Didn't sell. He started putting them in peck sacks, and offering a sack full for $2. But nobody would buy those screws, and Joe didn't understand why. Finally Joe asked a hardware dealer why he couldn't sell the cheapest screws in the country.

"You don't know?"

"No, sir, I don't."

"They have left-handed threads, Joe. That's why they are so damned cheap. Nobody wants to fool with left-handed screws."

And the hardware man shrugged and rolled his eyes at the ceiling and went back to sorting his right-handed screws.

It was a good time in America, and Americans were eager to read of it. Good living was descending on an Oklahoma fresh from the depths of a black depression and a bloody war – grateful to have lived through both of them. Jackie Robinson was cracking baseball's racial barrier with his booming bat, and in Oklahoma, a prominent Catholic bishop went to visit an unfortunate relative who had been confined in the insane asylum at Norman.

Horrified by what he saw there, the bishop called *The Daily Oklahoman* newspaper and asked them to do something about this insult to the human race. An aggressive kid named Mike Gorman drew the assignment. Gorman was a New Yorker who had spent his military time at Tinker Air Force Base, and when the war was over, he decided to stay in Oklahoma as a journalist. He drove down to Central State Hospital to see what had turned the bishop sick, and what he saw turned him sick, too. What he wrote about it sickened the nation.

Some Oklahomans wondered what all the fuss was about, still believing the insane were stricken into an irreversible subhuman state because of their own wickedness, and the worst of them, perhaps, possessed of demons. They wanted such creatures kept out of sight with thick iron bars assuring their evil could not escape into the countryside. Forgetting that they were somebody's cousins and brothers and sisters and moms and dads.

Oklahoma had four mental hospitals: Central State, Eastern State in Vinita, Western State in Fort Supply, and in Taft, old Governor Alfalfa Bill Murray had built the nation's only mental hospital of, by, and for Negroes, so no race mixing would happen even among the insane. Most buildings at all the institutions were old and run down, and all of them were overrun. There were 8,620 patients, Gorman wrote, many sleeping on mattresses thrown on the floor. On average there were four toilets and one bathtub for every 90 patients. Those who could not control their bowels or were too psychotic to know or care where and when to use the toilet were hosed down by aides when the stench became unbearable. Treatments were restraining sheets, sedatives, electro-shock and prefrontal lobotomies to make the patients more easily handled. Some of the aides were crazy as the inmates, more cruel maybe, and abusive. It was a sad and sickening thing with which to confront a state hungering for peace and prosperity. Good times for a change. There were other things to be done and seen. Oklahoma looked away.

❖

Dewey County is a neat rectangle in the next-to-last tier of western Oklahoma counties before the Texas Panhandle. It was named for Admiral George Dewey, although the only water in the county then was in three rivers: the South Canadian which loops through its middle, the North Canadian which nicks its northeast corner, and the Washita, which starts up somewhere in the southwest corner near Leedey. In between, it was high, dry, old wild-west country. Early railroads followed the cattle trails that were hellbent for Dodge City. Because of its rivers, Dewey County needed bridges for any kind of development. Especially Camargo.

Located just north of the South Canadian – biggest river in the county – Camargo needed a bridge as much as anybody ever needed a bridge. Camargo was so isolated that it could be reached from the nearest civilization only by a ferry raft tugged across the South Canadian River with a tractor, a rope, and a pulley. And such a device was an odd place for a boy from Peaceable Mountain to be, but there Joe sat in a car aboard the raft, trying to decide what he could say to these particular people to convince them Roy J. Turner should become the governor of Oklahoma when Robert S. Kerr's term expired.

Democratic candidates for public office then would hire smart, good-looking college students and send them out Saturdays when they were not in class to campaign. Joe was among a number of law students hired by Turner. Successful oilman and Oklahoma City civic leader, Turner had won the Democratic primary in a bitter runoff against Dixie Gilmer who had the support of some strong Democrats, including the Kerr family. Now, Turner was campaigning against Republican Olney F. Flynn and three independents. And Joe was having fun. Twenty-five dollars a day for making Saturday political speeches in favor of Democrats! More money than he had ever made. More than in the coal hellholes of Rock Springs, Wyoming. It was like being paid good money to breathe fresh air.

Joe had been startled by being greeted with a brass band in Boley, one of Oklahoma's all-black towns. The band was sponsored by Boley's famous Major McCormick. Major McCormick was in the same black fraternal fellowship as Joe's old friend, Major Seward, the blacksmith and black politician at McAlester. Both had been named honorary majors by Murray back in the 1930s. Both would have been called colonel if they had been white. McCormick had been the hero in thwarting a 1932 robbery of the Farmers and Merchants Bank at Boley by an associate of Pretty Boy Floyd's.

The way it came about was that Pretty Boy Floyd and George Birdwell had a Negro friend named Charlie Glass, and Glass wanted to show his white buddies how to rob a Negro bank. Pretty Boy declined the adventure, but Birdwell agreed. A second white man accompanied them, and the trio drove a Ford Roadster to the front of the bank, and Glass went in and tried to cash a check. The cashier asked for identification and, as they talked, Birdwell and the other white man slipped into the bank. Birdwell stepped behind the teller's cage and pointed his gun at bank President D.J. Turner and told him to scoop up the cash and hand it over.

McCormick, an assistant cashier at the time, saw what was happening and slipped into the bank's vault and got a rifle. Turner, as he handed over the money, sounded the bank's alarm. Birdwell shot him four times in the chest. McCormick opened fire from the door of the vault and killed Birdwell instantly. The second white bandit, unaware of where the bullets were coming from, grabbed the cash and ordered customers to carry Birdwell to the car. But black merchants in Boley had been through enough hard times to be ready for more. They were waiting outside, armed and ready. The second white man fell before their fire, and Glass ran for the car amid a sleet storm of bullets. One found Glass as he turned in the car seat to return fire. Murray declined to pay the Negro McCormick the $1,500 dead-or-alive reward he had offered for Birdwell, but named him an honorary major and gave him a job with the state. By 1946, when Joe had come to town to speak for Roy J. Turner, McCormick was superintendent of the Consolidated Negro Facility in Boley. But, he was no longer a Democratic Party hero.

He had supported Dixie Gilmer over Roy J. Turner in the primary election, and Gilmer had lost. McCormick was in imminent danger of losing his state job. And that is why he sent out a brass band to greet the man who came to town to speak for Roy J. Turner. Even if he was a first-year law student from Peaceable Mountain down deep in Pittsburg County.

Bill Murray had proved Major Seward right in his theory, though. He was so set against Negroes associating with whites in any way that he didn't even want white criminals associating with black criminals or crazy white people associating with crazy Negroes. So he built black institutions, at Boley, Taft, and Vinita, and he hired black people to run those institutions and that gave the Negroes more good jobs than anybody ever could have got for them by trying to help them.

After Boley, Joe's schedule had taken him to Vici, Shattuck, Leedey, and that is how he came to be sitting in the car on a ferry being tugged by a tractor across the South Canadian River to Camargo, trying desperately to think of something compelling to say to these people he had never seen in a place he had never been. It was there on the Camargo ferry that he came up with the first political promise of his career.

"If Roy J. Turner gets elected," he told the cheering crowd, "we will build the Camargo bridge across the South Canadian River."

Wade had chosen worse than Major McCormick in that primary election of 1946. William O. Coe had come to Ada early in the Democratic primary, and Wade was among the Negroes who stood back out of the way and listened to what this white man had to say. He didn't mention anything for Negroes, but he talked about equality. Common people. Working men. He was a veteran of the World War. Wade thought maybe he heard something in there that might trickle down to the Negro before it ran out, so he fiddled in his pocket and found $2, and he put it in the hat they passed around. And he inquired after the name of Coe's Negro campaign manager.

And again, Wade painted up his old pickup truck and got out his public address system and went around over the state, up at daybreak putting up signs, playing religious music and politicking in the black towns at night, and finally falling exhausted on the old mattress when everybody had stopped listening and gone home.

Coe ran fourth behind H.C. Jones with 61,216 votes.

Roy J. Turner became Oklahoma's 13th governor, replacing Robert S. Kerr who left office on January 13, 1947.

Nobody ever was able to determine for sure if it was because of what that young black-haired law student said about building a bridge across the Canadian River at Camargo, but Dewey County went for Roy J. Turner by 105 votes that year after going Republican in the three previous elections. Joe was among the first to be hired for his free Saturdays to form a statewide network of Young Citizens for Robert S. Kerr for the United States Senate in 1948.

Wade went back to hunting work in the daytime and playing cards at Mr. Finney's at night.

1948 *Prosperity and progress exploded. Production, employment, and income reached new highs. A two-bedroom house sold for $10,000, and they were being built in little rows, looking, a critic said, like a civilization hunkering down for survival. In their living rooms large wood cabinets began to appear with small screens on which live, moving pictures of the outside world could be seen from one's couch. Some brothers named McDonald started a new franchise for hamburger stands that used infrared heat lamps to keep French fries warm, and servicemen home from Italy demanded an exotic dish called pizza pie, causing the oregano market to skyrocket.*

President Harry Truman ended racial segregation in the military, denounced the Republican 80th Congress as the worst in history, and recognized the new state of Israel which came into being when Israeli terrorists forced the British to withdraw. The Russians blockaded Berlin, and the U.S. countered with an air lift. The old Indian peacemaker Mahatma Gandhi was shot, and to finish off all these beginnings and endings, Babe Ruth died.

And the old steam railroad locomotives loosed their last high, lonesome wail and were replaced by flat-blatting locomotives that ran on diesel, putting the coal mines around McAlester into a deeper slump.

16

The Mule Man

There was a Pittsburg County political race in 1930 that folks on Peaceable Mountain still talked about in 1948, as they still talked from time to time about the night Jimmy Braddock knocked out Max Baer and they got to hear the referee count him out on Dan Patty's radio – after J.I. ran for the bucket and watered down the ground wire.

Guy Andrews, a prominent McAlester lawyer, was trying for a second term in the Oklahoma State Senate. That wasn't done. Nobody ever had served two consecutive terms in the state Senate from Pittsburg County. A man named Pres Lester filed against Andrews. Pres Lester was a genius at political organizing. He had organized Pittsburg County down to the living rooms. He had a list that contained the name of one strong person in each of Pittsburg County's 79 precincts, and each of them had agreed to support Pres and those other candidates that Pres supported. They were called Pres's men, and they had in the past elected many a sheriff, county clerk, county commissioner.

And there was another long-standing tradition in Pittsburg County politics. Each of the candidates would get a hatchet man and put him in the race to cut up the other main candidate, so the main guys could remain gentlemen and be elected on the strength of their character. Pres Lester chose Carl Bernethie to cut up Guy Andrews. Carl was a little guy. Feisty. And he always wore a big, black hat. He was superintendent of the mule barn out at the state prison. Guy Andrews chose Alf Misenheimer, who ran a little newspaper down at Kiowa, to do the dirty work on Pres Lester. Carl and Alf were colorful individuals. Colorful speakers. But they got so mad at each other that they forgot all about Pres Lester and Guy Andrews and what they were in the race to do, and they went to cutting up each other.

Alf Meisenheimer – Guy Andrews' man – got to telling it that they caught Carl Bernethie – Pres Lester's man – showing an unacceptable level of affection for a mare mule out at the prison mule barn, and everybody got to giggling at the thought of the little guy in the big hat, and it got to be the talk of the county. At speakings, Meisenheimer would arrive a little late and when they would introduce him to speak, he would hesitate about coming up.

"Well, folks, I'm sorry I'm late," he would say. "but I heard the mule man was going to be here, and I am riding my mule. I didn't want to put her at risk, so I tied her up back there on the road and walked in."

That crowd would just go wild, and it was a consensus that Misenheimer defeated Bernethie in the hatchetman preliminary of that political fight. But Pres Lester beat Guy Andrews for the Senate seat anyway, because of his organization and the fact that nobody had ever served two terms in the Senate from Pittsburg County.

Hiram Impson loved to tell that story. Hi loved politics. He was an old-time newspaperman, a Choctaw Indian and a Democrat to the core. Editor of the McAlester newspaper. He had been and done just about everything. Postmaster. National Guard. Served in the Oklahoma Legislature. In 1948, Plowboy Edwards was one of Pittsburg County's representatives in the Oklahoma House of Representatives and had been since defeating Elmer Tompkins back in 1942, the one-term jinx having never applied to the House. Plowboy was a Democrat, but he wasn't one of Hi Impson's Democrats. Hi had served in the House with Plowboy and had come away with something less than affection for him. In 1948, Hi Impson was desperately combing Pittsburg County for someone to run against Plowboy Edwards. Feelings were running high. Those who knew politics could feel a good, old-fashioned revival stirring. Robert S. Kerr had successfully finished out his term as Oklahoma's first native-born governor, and was in a hot campaign for the U.S. Senate.

Carl Albert, young intellectual phenomenon from a coal miner's shanty in the small Pittsburg County community of Bug Tussle, had come home from the war, filed as a candidate for the Third Congressional District seat in 1946 and won. He was a little bitty kid with freckles, and he dressed like a dandy, but he had the voice of a giant and a mind that could see things coming before anybody else could see them. Other young veterans home from the war were going to college and filing for legislative offices all over the state. And Hi Impson was desperate to get on the bandwagon with a good candidate to defeat Plowboy Edwards.

Joe headed home for a couple of days before starting his final summer term of law school. If his schedule held, he would be practicing law in his own office in McAlester by the time he turned 21 in October of that year of 1948. And he just might not come home by himself. His brother, Jack, had introduced him to the prettiest woman Joe had ever seen.

Her name was Agnes Leota Minter. She had been away to Washington to work during the war, and she was older than Joe, and she did not act like the other girls Joe had met. Only one thing bothered him about her. Agnes Leota Minter was not at all impressed with Injin Joe Stipe from Peaceable Mountain. Or did not appear to be so.

When he arrived home, Joe dropped by the *McAlester News-Capital* office to pick up a newspaper and listen for a while to Hi Impson's stories. But this weekend, Hi was serious.

"Joe, I want you to run for the legislature against Plowboy Edwards."

Joe laughed.

"Hi, I'm not even 21 years old."

"When is your birthday?"

"October."

"That'll do. I want you to run against Plowboy Edwards."

Joe had to admit to himself that he didn't know for sure what the legislature was. Knew there was one. He kept telling Hi that campaigning for Robert S. Kerr on free Saturdays was a long way from running for political office himself, and, besides, he didn't know how Mr. Kerr would take it if he quit in the middle of the campaign and started one of his own. But Hi kept on at him every time he went by the newspaper, and Joe started to go by the newspaper office more and more often. Finally, Joe laid the case before Robert S. Kerr.

"Joe, your running for office is a lot more important. My campaign is in good shape. You've been a lot of help to me. I'll even help you some."

❖

Wade was up early, waiting around the house for the dew to dry off the grass. He finally had found himself a way to make an honest living, but clouds lay dark and threatening off to the southwest of Ada, and he had a lot of work to do today if he was going to make it as an Oklahoma hay hauler.

Mr. Finney, in addition to his grocery store and the gambling game in back, had a big farm and a lot of hay that needed to be gathered from the field and hauled. Wade had been wanting an old truck to take to the California watermelon fields and get rich, so he borrowed money from Mr. Finney and made a down payment on a 1938 Chevrolet. Black. Bobtail. Dual rear wheels. When Mr. Finney's hay had been cut and baled, Wade would drive the truck down through town after the dew was off and pick up some friends lounging on the street. They all would go to the hay meadow and Wade would creep the truck across the field while one man rode the truckbed to stack and the other men threw the hay onto the truck. When the truck was loaded, they would haul it to one of Mr. Finney's barns and stack it inside against the weather. And Wade could make a living, and his friends got a little walking-around money.

Mr. Finney had gotten Wade a job loading and hauling 600 bales of hay for one of the other farmers around Ada. Do good on this and Wade could become Ada's premier hay hauler. But, if the morning dew can ruin hay stored too wet, rain ruins freshly baled hay right where it lies in the field, and on this day, the clouds were promising rain. Wade cruised the old bobtail truck from joint to joint, but he couldn't find any buddies. Around noon, he found one in a tavern about half drunk. Shortly after noon, he found another, and that one was completely drunk, and Wade could feel the air beginning to change. He rushed home and got his wife.

"You drive the truck," he pleaded. "I'll pitch bales. It won't do to lose that man's hay."

Working easily under the cool of the clouds, Wade would throw a few bales up and then climb up and stack them, motioning for his wife to ease the truck forward. He got 66 bales loaded before it started to sprinkle rain, and before he could get into the cab, it opened up and poured. Wade raced for the man's barn with the 66 bales, but the last hill before the barn was clay and steep and slick. Wade made three tries at it and ended up in the ditch three times.

He threw off the 66 bales to get loose from that hill and went back to town.

And word was around Ada by morning that 66 of the man's bales were soaking in a ditch beside the road and 534 were soaked in the field. Wade's hay hauling days in Ada were over. But, he figured, he had his truck for the California watermelon fields.

❖

"Joe disappeared."

Agnes shrugged it to her curious girlfriends. "He said he was going to run for state representative, and he just disappeared."

And she wished, perhaps, she had not tried so hard to be unimpressed with the handsome young law student from Peaceable Mountain with the wry, dimpled smile.

"There was something about him," she would confide in his absence. "He was different than the others. Relaxed. If he was in a room, you just felt it. And he was so proud of his family, had a close family background. My parents are – were – quite taken with him."

What she did not try to tell them was that she had never met anybody like him before, and she couldn't put into words even to herself what the difference was. Oh, she could say he was tall and handsome and intelligent and that his grin was infectious and that he was fun. But that wasn't what it was. The thing that really set him apart from the others was a feeling. Of safety. Of a solid something being there with her own best interests in mind. Something that would not change with the wind. When they had started dating and before anything was serious, a leaky gas stove had almost asphyxiated her and her girlfriend. And he could not study or work or be at ease with himself until he had put her in a safe place – moved her heavy things to a new apartment with his own awkward hands. And when she was safe and cared for, he had left and stayed gone until he had caught back up the things that had got behind during his nursing. And there were no expectations. It was as if he had forgotten it had happened.

Joe had no idea what he was doing. He had never even had his name in the newspaper except when he came home from the Navy. Hi Impson told him that getting his name in the paper was important.

"If you are the first to file your papers of candidacy," Impson told him, "first in the entire state, *The Daily Oklahoman* probably will put your picture in the paper."

Joe headed for Oklahoma City on the Sunday evening before the filing period opened on Monday, prepared to wait all night if he had to in order to be the first to file. But, somebody was ahead of him. A dapper man, talkative. He was, he said, Victor Wickersham, filing for election to Congress from western Oklahoma's Seventh Congressional District. Re-election, actually, he said. He was elected congressman in 1941 at a special election to replace Sam Massingale who had died after six years in office. Wickersham had been re-elected in 1942 and 1944, but he was defeated in 1946. He was here, he said, to claim his seat back, and being first in line would get his picture in the paper. Glumly, Joe got in line behind him.

So it was that J.I. Stipe's blackheaded boy from Peaceable Mountain waited all night with dapper former U.S. Congressman Victor Wickersham on the off-chance that he would leave or fall down or that the newspaper would run the pictures of the first two filing. The filing papers Joe held in his hand said nothing about a blackheaded kid known as Injin Joe Stipe. They said he was a young law student named Gene Stipe.

Joe had selected the name carefully. He couldn't run for public office with a name like Injin Joe. And he sure wasn't going to run as Eugene Earl. He didn't like Eugene and he didn't like Earl. In the Navy, he had signed his name E.E., and his fellow midshipmen called him E Square or Ed. But, when he decided to run for office he had done some research. A governor of Georgia whom Joe admired was named Gene Talmadge. His full name was Eugene. Further research showed all the Genes in the political world seemed to have been named Eugene originally. And that is how Joe signed the filing papers. Gene Stipe. It seemed odd.

When the office finally opened and Wickersham had filed, Joe stepped up to the counter. Bill Cordell, secretary of the election board, studied his papers and waved him aside.

"I need to talk to you, son."

Over where nobody else could hear.

"I can't accept these papers," he said, "you've got to be 21 years old to hold office in Oklahoma."

"I will be 21 by the time I hold office."

And Bill Cordell scratched his head.

"Why don't you go down and get an opinion from the attorney general?"

And Joe made the long walk down the stairs to the office of the venerable Mac Q. Williamson who had been attorney general longer than any other man in Oklahoma history, and who was at that moment in a hurry to make the long walk up the stairs Joe had just walked down and file as an opponent to Robert S. Kerr for the U.S. Senate seat. It was an off year for him and a loss would hurt nothing but his pride.

"Tell me, young man," he said, "just exactly how you want this thing to come out."

The young law school student was startled.

"Well, sir, it appears to me that if I am 21 before the general election, sir, that is what should count."

"Why, just among us Rebekahs, I think that's the law."

And Mac Q. called Bill Cordell and told him he would write the opinion, and Bill Cordell went ahead and filed Joe's papers. So Joe ended up filing second, but he got his picture in the paper,

anyway. Joe decided if his political career ever amounted to anything, Mac Q. Williamson was the kind of friend he wanted to
have. And to be.

On Wednesday night, when the filing period ended, Joe got a
telephone call. It was Robert S. Kerr.

"Meet me at the airport tomorrow morning at six o'clock."

The small, single-engine plane bounced onto the runway right
on time, and it seemed like it took five minutes for the big man to
unfold out of it. It was Robert S. Kerr. He was holding an envelope.
It contained one thousand dollars in cash. Joe had never seen such
a thing, but he took it home and told J.I. he thought he might try
to get used to it. And he decided right there that Robert S. Kerr
sure enough was his friend and if there was ever anything he could
ever do for Bob Kerr he was going to do it.

Thus Injin Joe, J.I. Stipe's blackheaded cook and firewood cut-
ter from Peaceable Mountain, became a bona fide candidate for the
House of Representatives of the State of Oklahoma named Gene
Stipe. Complete with a campaign war chest of one thousand dollars. Joe couldn't believe it.

17

Who's that Boy Stompin' that Flag?

On a hot afternoon in the summer of 1948, a big car pulled up to the high front porch of the Binger Trading Company in Binger, Oklahoma, out west in Caddo County, a long way from Pittsburg County and a long way from the political fights in Oklahoma City. The trading post was owned by two brothers. An older brother Lloyd and a younger brother Dean. Dean was sweeping the porch when the big car arrived. He leaned on his broom and peered down into the car where a big man with a built-in air of authority sat in the passenger seat beside his sweating driver. Dean had heard about a new gimmick that was supposed to bolt under the dashboard and cool the air inside an automobile, but it had not reached Oklahoma yet, and nobody was sure whether it would even work, but this day in Binger, Oklahoma, he thought, would have been a good day to find out.

"Well, hi, governor!" boomed Dean, "Get out and come in."

But former Oklahoma governor Robert S. Kerr was in a political race as hot as the day, and, as usual, he was in a hurry.

"No," he said, "you tell Lloyd I said to come out here."

Dean hurried through the store toward where his brother sat working, wearing his cowboy boots, right shoulder drooping slightly, white cowboy hat on the edge of the battered old desk.

The visit was no surprise. Lloyd's political advice and support had been sought in Caddo County since he had been little more than a boy and had driven old Bill Murray all over western Oklahoma in his 1929 campaign for governor. After working for Murray as relief administrator in Custer County in 1932, Lloyd Rader had gone to work for the Oklahoma Tax Commission, rising to chief of the general enforcement department of the commission. By 1939, however, he had had his fill of state government work, and he had resigned to return to Binger and open the Trading Company with his brother.

Dean knew former Governor Robert S. Kerr because his brother had handled northern Caddo County for Kerr in the political campaign that made him governor in 1942. Lloyd had done the same for Roy J. Turner in 1946, and he had turned both men down when they asked him to come to work for them, because he had no further appetite for state employment. He rarely went anywhere near the capitol even to visit old friends. Dean was breathing hard by the time he reached his brother.

"Lloyd? Bob Kerr said to tell you to come out front."

Lloyd Rader had access to a cold, blue-baleful look that could freeze a horse in mid-stride. And he gave that look now to his brother.

"You tell that dough-bellied s.o.b. that if he wants to talk to me, he can come in here."

"Lloyd, its Governor Kerr!"

"And you tell him just the way I said it."

Dean eased back out onto the porch.

"What did he say, Dean?"

"Uh, governor? He said for you to come on in."

"Oh, he did? And what were his exact words?"

"You really want to know?"

"Yes, I do."

"He said, 'You tell that dough-bellied s.o.b. that if he wants to talk to me, he can come in here."

Kerr's laugh boomed the length of the small-town street.

"I told you," he said to his driver, " I told you that was what he'd say. We might as well get out."

And former governor Robert S. Kerr walked down the aisle of the Binger Trading Company and up to the battered old desk for a warm reunion with a Democratic political ally who had become much more than that. After leaving the store, Kerr was quiet for a long time in the car.

Someday, he finally told the driver, somebody is going to get Lloyd Rader back into state government, and that would be a stroke of luck for them and for the state of Oklahoma. If not the United States. Lloyd Rader was just that kind of a man.

That summer of 1948 was a political scorcher not only in Oklahoma but in the nation. President Harry S. Truman – seeking his first full term after ascending to the presidency at the death of President Roosevelt – made a whirlwind tour of the state, giving 22 speeches in two days. Kerr was one of ten Oklahoma Democrats in a blistering race to see who could recapture the U.S. Senate seat that had been won in 1942 by Republican E.H. Moore. Unlike the others, former Governor Robert S. Kerr hooked his campaign for the U.S. Senate to the campaign train of the peppery haberdasher from Kansas City, Mo.

❖

The campus of the University of Oklahoma also shook with change that year. Ada Lois Sipuel Fisher applied to become the first Negro to attend the University of Oklahoma School of Law. She said what Wade had learned so painfully back in 1939. There was no segregated black college in Oklahoma that offered what she needed for a degree in law.

Joe had become a leader in the Independent Students Association, a rebel group that thumbed its nose at the traditional Greek fraternities. A fiery young rabblerouser from Sapulpa named John Young was elected president of the Student Senate. Everything boiled into a series of student demonstrations that rocked the placid campus. *The Daily Oklahoman* newspaper published an infuriating picture of a student stomping the flag of the United States of America. Oklahoma was outraged. Especially a man named Collins P. Edwards

Collins P. Edwards lived in Pittsburg County. He originally was from Mississippi as were many of the people of Pittsburg County. Many of their neighbors came from Alabama and Georgia and Tennessee. Most of them were farmers or had been farmers or were sons of farmers. Farming still was the most noble occupation of their time, along with coal mining, at least in Pittsburg County, and Collins P. Edwards was an adroit politician. So he called himself Plowboy. Said the name came directly from his old daddy. When he entered politics, he stopped signing his name as Collins P. Edwards, and he started signing it C. Plowboy Edwards, and it worked. It got him elected to the House of Representatives from Pittsburg County in 1942, and it had got him through every election since then, and now it seemed sure to get him successfully past a challenge from a college kid from Peaceable Mountain that nobody knew.

Joe had been little seen in McAlester since leaving it for the war in the summer of 1943. He had come home from college only about once a month when he and Jack could trade off a weekend with someone at the fire station and drive from Norman to McAlester in the family Jeep. Nobody knew him much anymore except for the Cables and the Stipes and Dan Patty and a few other folks out on Peaceable Mountain. Most voters had never seen him, and now there was the name problem. People who did know him knew him as Joe or Eugene Earl and not as a political candidate named Gene. The election was to be in July. C. Plowboy Edwards snipped out the picture *The Daily Oklahoman* had published of that student stomping the American flag. He folded it, and put it in his pocket.

"I don't know this boy that is running against me," he'd say when he was out talking with folks on the street. And he'd reach into his pocket and pull out that picture. "But I think that's him, stomping that flag."

At "speakings," Plowboy would tell the folks he was also afraid that this boy who was running against him might be planning to send Negro kids to the white schools in McAlester. Plowboy went to every schoolhouse and every community in Pittsburg County. And he showed them the picture. And he voiced his Mississippi concerns about what would happen if this boy tried to send the Negro kids to the white schools in McAlester. And he felt pretty easy about the upcoming election.

But, things were happening about which Collins Plowboy Edwards had no way of knowing.

After Pres Lester and Carl Bernethie survived Alf Meisenheimer's story about Carl and the mare mule at the prison, Pres had served out his term in the state Senate and gone home, but he had never stopped organizing Pittsburg County Democrats. By the time young Gene Stipe's name was formally recorded as a candidate in the office of Bill Cordell, Pres was elderly, kind of an invalid, almost blind. He was living in Oklahoma City with his daughter and son-in-law, Otis Sullivant, legendary political writer for *The Daily Oklahoman* and right-hand man to arch-conservative E.K. Gaylord. But Pres still controlled the closest thing to a Democratic political machine that there ever was in Pittsburg County. And he still had that list of Pres's men.

Hi Impson took Joe to Otis Sullivant's house in Oklahoma City, and Pres and Hi sat down with that list and updated it, removing the names of the dead. And Pres presented it to Joe.

"All you've got to tell them," he said, "is that Pres sent you."

"Dammit Wade! Can't you make this ol' truck stand still?"

For the second time that morning, the clutch-shudder of the old truck had sent the delicately balanced California watermelons tumbling, and the pitching boys had to jump back up there and put them back again before they could get on a full load.

"Come on, fellas, I need this load bad."

And because Wade had picked beside them in the California watermelon fields since he was a boy and now owned his own truck and might make something of himself the pitching boys started stacking again.

Seventy-five dollars to haul one load 112 miles to Los Angeles, and there would be people waiting there to unload them. Wade sat in the cab of the truck and considered. Beat Oklahoma hay hauling any day of the week. When the boys finally stopped stacking, the old truck was groaning under six tons of watermelon.

"Now Wade," said the foreman, "these watermelons are perishable produce. You got to get to Los Angeles with them and you got to get there with them today. Anything happen, you call us."

"Yessir. Ain't nothing gonna happen to them watermelons."

And now, Wade watched the miles spin money through the speedometer. Gas 22 cents a gallon, 112 miles to Los Angeles. Seventy five dollars when he got there. Gonna be some money made today. When he got within 20 miles of Los Angeles, he began to relax. To laugh into the hot California wind. It was not going to rain on Wade Watts today. Not in California.

Pow! Like a shotgun. Out went one of them duals, and six tons of watermelons suddenly were riding on one skinny little old tire. Wade fought the old truck to the side of the road, jumped out almost before it stopped moving and scrambled to jack it up to get the load off that one skinny tire.

Pow! And the load was setting on the rim. Wade Watts, California watermelon hauler, was sitting beside the road in the hot sun with a load of perishable produce. Reluctantly, he hitched a ride to a filling station and called Blythe. Rule was, you break down, you give your load away.

"Thanks, buddy."

The new driver grinned at him. This white guy with good tires would haul Wade's watermelons the remaining 20 miles to Los Angeles and Wade's $75 all the way back to Blythe and Wade would never see none of it. Glumly, he finished jacking up the truck, put on his spare and went on back to Blythe and bought another tire.

"Come on, guys, you can load me. She'll stand still."

Major Seward was overjoyed. J.I. Stipe's black-headed boy – who used to come by the blacksmith shop with his daddy when he wasn't this high – was running for the Oklahoma Legislature under his real name of Gene Stipe. Before he even finished law school. Going to unseat Plowboy Edwards as the new state representative from McAlester. That boy would be a friend to the Negro sure. Major Seward got hold of the candidate right off and told him he wanted to throw him a goat barbecue. Make sure everybody knew that the Gene Stipe on the ballot was J.I. Stipe's boy, Joe.

When the young candidate made his appearance, there was a rousing round of applause. Major Seward ceremoniously handed him the first barbecued goat sandwich, and Gene ceremoniously bit into it. He never had liked goat, but if it was barbecued long enough and he was hungry enough he had been able to take it. This time, goat hair came out in his teeth.

Now, in the Pittsburg County of the late 1940s, there was a common expression used by polite men under extreme duress to relieve themselves. It was called going to the chimney corner. A chimney corner was where an outside wall joined the out-jutting chimney, and it was so constructed that a man could step discreetly into it and nobody could see what he did there. Plowboy Edwards, himself, had made the chimney corner a part of the political language when he had run a campaign against Ben Choate. Ben had introduced a bill to put a tax on public pay toilets.

"Ben Choate wants to tax your toilets!"

Plowboy had hammered him with it, and the crowds had loved it.

"Chimney Corner Ben," he named him.

Said as long as Ben Choate was in office, the only place you could go relieve yourself without paying a tax was the chimney corner. And Plowboy Edwards and the chimney corner had defeated Ben Choate. And that was the man challenged by J.I. Stipe's black-headed boy who stood now before his first political gathering with goat hair in his teeth and sickness swelling in his stomach.

"Major Seward," he said, "I've got to go to the chimney corner."

And he ran out the door and around the side of the building and into the chimney corner and threw the sandwich away and spit out what was left of it in his mouth. Then he stayed a reasonable length of time and got his stomach settled and went back inside and told the Major how good the sandwich was. Made a little speech to the crowd about how good it was. Winced and said it. It was, after all, his first political sandwich. Hair and all.

And throughout the campaign, Gene let Plowboy do all the talking about Negroes going to school with the white folks. Gene just kept making the speakings, and he kept calling on the strong old men and women who were on that list of Pres Lester's. The postmaster at Ulan. Mr. Harraway over at Quinton.

"Pres sent me."

It was magic.

Wade squatted low to the sidewalk and peered into the Los Angeles barber shop. Like the undercover policemen had said, none of the two or three fellows sitting in there looked anything at all like Charlie Red. But they had one fellow in the barber chair with a towel around his face. Brand new shoes. Charlie Red hadn't had any brand new shoes. But that was before Wade's money had come up gone.

Wade had given Charlie Red a ride from Ada to California and had fed him all summer while Charlie hunted for work. Wade knew better than to give Charlie Red money, but fed him and gave him a place to sleep. Wade had given up trying to longhaul watermelons in his old bobtail truck and settled for hauling them from the fields to the railroad in Blythe where they were loaded onto trains. He hadn't gotten rich, but as the end of summer neared he had counted up his money, and it came to $351 in small bills rolled up in a wad to take home with him to Ada. And he had put the money away and when he went back for it, it was gone. And so was Charlie Red. And Charlie hadn't come for dinner. Or breakfast.

"He come by here the night before last. Man, he had a roll of money, it might not choke a horse, but it would choke a pony down," the big-eyed man told Wade. "He just spreaded it out. Made a green carpet on my bed. He left here going to Chicago."

"Los Angeles." The man's wife shot him a look. "He didn't say Chicago, he said Los Angeles."

Wade went to the chief of police at Blythe.

"Sorry, fella, can't do anything about it if he's outta the county."

But Wade looked so beat down for losing his whole summer's work to a friend like Charlie Red that the policeman gave him $5 to use to keep looking for him. Wade put the $5 together with $15 borrowed from a friend and pointed the old truck toward Los Angeles.

"Did you get a warrant from Blythe?" said the Los Angeles desk sergeant.

"I don't know nothing about no warrant."

"Well, hell, by God, we can't go around here putting people in jail just because you say to put them in there. You have to have a warrant or something."

And Wade's temper finally snapped.

"You say you ain't gon arrest him? I say you will. You gon arrest me and him both before this day's over. I know where he is and I'm going after my money. Right now."

Wade had called his wife in Ada and had her go to Charlie Red's people there and find out the address of his kin in Los Angeles. And it was 3232 South Central Avenue, Apartment 2. And that is where Wade was going. Police or no police.

The sergeant let him get to the door before he figured out Wade meant what he said, and that was when he had called him back and summoned the two black detectives in plain clothes to go with him.

Charlie Red's old auntie had opened the door.

"Yeah, he come over here several times, all dressed up. He just left here a little while ago, said he was going down to the barber shop."

The detectives had told Wade to wait in the car while they went in to see if anybody matched Wade's description of Charlie. They had come back saying they drew a blank, but that there was one man in the chair with a towel over his face. And all of that is why Wade was squatting on the sidewalk in Los Angeles looking into a barber shop.

Finally, the barber pulled the towel off the face of the man in the chair, and Wade raced back to the car where the detectives were waiting.

"That's him! That's Charlie Red in the barber chair!"

At Charlie Red's new apartment, it took only two cuts upside the head with the detective's billy club and Charlie told it all. After two days of being a bigshot, he had $14 left of the $351 Wade had spent the summer working for. The detectives searched the apartment, gave Wade a new suit they found there, two pair of pants and two pair of new shoes and a new hat. And Wade started one more trip home broke from California, but at least he was dressed well and had an extra pair of shoes. But, he had to pay part of the $14 to have the pants taken up.

Agnes Leota Minter finally got a call from her missing Pittsburg County boyfriend.

"I won!"

"So what?"

They had a nice wedding in January, 1949, in the First Baptist Church of Chickasha, Dr. W. A. Criswell, pastor of the First Baptist Church of Dallas, Texas, presiding.

Bob Bates had filed against a man from South Oklahoma City who did not learn his debate at school. He was tough. His name was J.D. McCarty.

part three

The Orange Bowl in Miami, Florida. On the field, the Alabama Crimson Tide with Sophomore quarterback Joe Namath leading the offense was mauling the Oklahoma Sooners. And in the VIP section, Oklahoma's fire-haired young governor J. Howard Edmondson was watching the game and talking politics with a personal friend, John F. Kennedy, President of the United States. There was a stir. The governor of Oklahoma rose suddenly and hurried with his entourage toward the exit. Something had happened. Something big enough to pull a young governor away from the President of the United States and an OU ball game that hadn't been finished.

18

Uncle Oren Goes International

"Go see Harry Bailey."

Governor Roy J. Turner, shrugged, said it over his shoulder to the new first-term House member from Pittsburg County.

"Tell him what you want, not me. He's the highway director."

And State Representative Gene Stipe walked over to meet Mr. Harry Bailey face to face for the first time. Gene had told Governor Turner he had some highway workers in his district that were not especially supportive of him after he had defeated their old friend and patron, C. Plowboy Edwards, by a margin, almost, of two to one. He had told the governor he would like to change some of them out. Pull out some opponents, he said, and replace them with some friends.

"What in hell do you mean telling me what you want to do?"

Gene couldn't believe what he was hearing. The little guy was red in the face, was waving his arms, had a mustache like Adolph Hitler's, and at the moment, was acting like him.

"I'm director of the Oklahoma Department of Highways!"

Mr. Bailey had come to Oklahoma in 1930 – when Gene was about four years old – to design and oversee construction of the Frisco Railroad Depot in south Oklahoma City's Capitol Hill. He had stayed around and had become personal friends with such men as Bob Kerr, Roy J. Turner, other millionaires. He had been a successful city manager of Oklahoma City, and by the time Gene walked into his office, he was known as Mr. Highways in Oklahoma. The man to talk with about roads. But obviously not in the way Gene did.

"You are a first-term House member from Pittsburg County. I will run this department."

"Yes, sir. I understand, sir," Gene said, although he didn't. The red-faced Bailey finally stopped waving his arms, walked to his desk and sat down. Stared at him until Gene dropped his eyes. Then he sat forward.

"Now," he said, "who was it you wanted to change out?"

And he went ahead and did what Gene wanted him to do, and Gene left there thinking that he really would like to have H.E. Bailey as his friend, even if he did look like Adolph Hitler. Gene knew for sure he didn't want him as an enemy.

Uncle Oren went to Ethiopia. And, again, it was because of Dr. Henry Bennett, president of Oklahoma A&M College – one of the most exceptional men in Oklahoma history, although not so much was made of him as was made of others. Henry Garland Bennett was born in December of 1886 and spent about half his life going to school and the other half passing what he learned on to others. He was a big-viewed man, long-range planner.

He took over as president of Oklahoma A&M College in 1928 when it was a small land-grant college specializing in agriculture and mechanics, and he turned it into a modern university, and in the process he developed the best political organization that had existed to that time in Oklahoma. It was a simple thing – the County Agricultural Extension Service – and therein lay its wisdom.

Dr. Bennett had a county agent and a county home demonstration agent in each of the 77 courthouses in Oklahoma, and a vo-ag teacher with a chapter of Future Farmers of American in almost every school district. His folks offered real-life stuff. County agents taught how you cross breed cattle, breed jacks to mares and get big mules, and such. Home demonstration agents taught canning and not getting poisoned and other aspects of developing a quality home life for rural families. The vocational agriculture teacher was kind of a jack of all trades, veterinarian, crop specialist. Most had columns in the weekly paper.

So if Dr. Bennett wanted to get the word out, "We want to support Bob Kerr for governor," he'd make some calls, and everybody down the line would make a few calls, and in about ten minutes it would be all over Oklahoma. He could get the word out across the state quicker than the newspapers could.

Just about everybody went to Dr. Bennett on political matters. He probably elected Bob Kerr as governor without ever taking to the back of a pickup truck or making a single political promise. Same, probably, with Governor Roy Turner, Red Phillips.

The County Agricultural Extension Program was a cooperative project. The federal government put in a third of the money, the state put in a third and the counties put in a third. Dr. Bennett didn't invent it, but he developed it into an awesome organization.

And because of all that, Oklahoma A&M was recognized as the pre-eminent educational facility of the state. So it was no real surprise when Harry Truman called Dr. Bennett to Washington in late 1948, right after he was elected President of the United States in his own right. He asked Dr. Bennett to administer a program of American help for undeveloped countries that had come under U.S. protection at the end of the World War, and for other hungry countries around the world that were in danger of being lured into communism. It was the fourth point of President Truman's inaugural speech.

Dr. Bennett took experts from Oklahoma A&M and sent them all over the world, and they carried Oklahoma A&M's idea of extension in agriculture with them. Instead of buying friendships, they earned them for America by sharing what they knew. One of them was Uncle Oren who had taught Joe how to turn a hickory bush into a pecan tree.

And that was how Uncle Oren got from Peaceable Mountain to Ethiopia.

The 34-year-old superintendent of schools at Red Oak, east of McAlester in Latimer County, had been elected to the legislature in 1946, the year Gene got out of the Navy. He was neither a veteran nor all that young, but he drove right through McAlester on his way from Red Oak to the state capitol in Oklahoma City for legislative sessions, and since Gene had no car, the educator invited the young first-termer to ride with him. That way, he said, he would have somebody to talk to on the long drive. And he did. Gene would ask him the time and he would give him the history of the clock (from the Middle English clokke, Gene, and or from the Old North French cloque, meaning bell and or from Middle Dutch clocke, meaning bell, clock, both from Medieval Latin clocca, of imitative origin.) He was a great conversationalist, great detail man, a great historian. Mostly, he talked education. Talked it all the time. With his hands anchored to the steering wheel, he would take Gene wandering throughout Oklahoma's history from clear back when Oklahoma was a territory. He had been a teacher at age 18. A principal at 23. County superintendent of Latimer County schools from 1938 to 1942, and high school inspector for the Oklahoma State Department of Education from 1942 until 1945. He liked to tell how it felt to have to ride a cowpony through a sleet storm just to get to high school. What would have happened to him if there had been no men around like Jay Pepper, John Prock, and J.O. Rich who saw that he needed help and gave it. What it must be like for kids who knew no such men.

His name was E.T. Dunlap. And he was driven to pass on what had been given to him.

"I have this idea," he said, "growing up over at Cravens, back in the hills miles from a high school…" And then he would tell about building the new high school for Buffalo Valley and then discovering how many Oklahoma children were not going to high school, and how 12 years of education should be at the doorstep of every kid in Oklahoma. That, he said, was what brought him to the Oklahoma Legislature.

In those days the Oklahoma Legislature met once every two years. During E.T.'s first session in 1947, the Legislature had set up the Oklahoma State Legislative Council, a standing committee of 15 House members and ten senators who were to meet between sessions to study problems of state government and make recommendations to the other legislators when they gathered back in. The speaker of the House had appointed E.T. to the new organization, and the group had made him chairman of its Committee on Education. The position was ready-made for what E.T. Dunlap was there to do.

He had spent the 18 months before the opening of his second legislative session dissecting the problem that had dogged him since he had ridden that little cowpony through the ice storm to Jay Pepper's store. His legislative council committee had found more than 1,300 laws and pieces of laws and court decisions and attorney general's opinions that were supposed to guide the Oklahoma educational system. It was a confused mess. He hired a friend from the University of Oklahoma – Dr. Ross Pugmire – to help as a professional; Mac Q. Williamson – still Oklahoma's perpetual attorney general after his run at the U.S. Senate failed – allowed the committee the use of one of his assistants, J. Harry Johnson. They put all the laws and pieces of laws and court decisions and attorney general's opinions into one pile and sifted out the parts that were good. They included them – and the new laws needed to make them work – into an Oklahoma School Code containing 23 articles, 326 typewritten pages, legal-sized, double-spaced. It was the biggest bill ever presented to the Oklahoma Legislature and the first so-called code. It was designed to take all the laws on one subject and put them together in an understandable way. And it involved one of the most volatile political issues in rural Oklahoma – school consolidation.

"It will cut the number of school districts in Oklahoma from 4,451 to about 600, wiping out all of the little former elementary school districts that are no longer operating a school. That will raise the hackles of citizens in those districts who have been voting only a very small millage and then transferring their children to a nearby school district for a small transfer fee. Every school district will also be a transportation district and that means that every kid in that district who wants to go to high school…".

Gene grinned and looked off out the car window as the fields alongside the road began settling down and turning flatter – hills subsiding into little rolling mounds of blackjack timber – as the countryside made its way from the edge of the Ozarks to the crosstimbers near the center of the state.

What this scholarly fellow was saying was that he was determined to send bright, shiny new school buses into every backwoods hill and holler in the State of Oklahoma. All the Cravenses. All the Peaceable Mountains. To all those little kids in ducking jumpers with no lining. He was, he said, ready to put his new legislative career – and anybody else's who would go with him – on the line in what would be a brawl with Oklahoma's rural political system to get it done.

"It will cost money, Gene. It is going to be a fight. Opposition will develop. You can bet on it. Opposition will develop. Those old rural boys," said the legislator from Red Oak, Oklahoma, "will fight us."

Finally, E.T. stopped talking and looked across the front seat of the car at Gene.

"Will you help me sponsor it?"

"Me?"

"Yes."

"I'm just a freshman, E.T."

"I'm going to need all the help I can get."

"My friends tell me school consolidation can beat us all."

"It might."

Gene got to thinking then how it was to have that schoolbus come over Peaceable Mountain. How it turned his life around, got him ready in the best way Savanna could to keep up with brilliant kids like Bob Bates and Johnny Carson at Millsap College and at the University of South Carolina.

"It is revolutionary," he explained to his wife, Agnes. "It will cut the number of school districts drastically. Make all of them responsible for getting school buses out to all kids in their district. It could beat us. I think I will go with E.T. on it."

Thus it was that the young first-termer became a co-sponsor of the most revolutionary public education bill in the state's history. And he did it in the car between McAlester and Oklahoma City with the superintendent of schools at Red Oak, Oklahoma, who used to have to ride his cowpony through a sleetstorm to get to high school.

They fought through legislation to put a bus to high school within reach of just about every kid in Oklahoma. Roy J. Turner signed the bill, and it didn't beat either one of them. And that is how it came to be that every student in Oklahoma who finishes elementary school, now is guaranteed the chance to finish high school.

❖

There are two significant memorials to dead heroes in McAlester, both in Shattuck Park. One is a memorial to soldiers who have died in the line of duty in America's wars. The other is for the coal miners who died in their line of duty, digging coal. There are more dead miners than dead soldiers.

Gene spent most of his time that first year writing into legislation things learned directly and indirectly from men like coal miner Pete Hanraty, vice president of the Oklahoma Constitutional Convention (who once had been mayor of McAlester) and J.I. Stipe.

Because of the battles of men like Hanraty, the state mine inspector and all of his assistants were elected statewide to prevent the coal companies from regaining control of the mine inspectors. John M. Malloy, the chief state mine inspector, lived in Alderson and was a good friend of the Stipe family.

The first piece of legislation Gene put together – with the help of men whose blackened hands proved they knew whereof they spoke – was the state's first comprehensive Mine Safety Act.

19

Death of a Mother Road

Roads, like trains, tend to be romantic. They so often start for the traveler at a place he is tired of and go to a place he has never been. And there never has been a road in America as romantic as old Route 66. In a time when many people had never been out of their county, U.S. Highway 66 started at Grant Park in Chicago and reached across more than 2,400 miles, three time zones and eight states before it dead-ended at Santa Monica Boulevard and Ocean Avenue in Santa Monica, California. Route 66 inspired songs. And, it ushered the world and its spending money past the doorsteps of all the little tourist courts and restaurants that had sprung up in a young Oklahoma with a depression still fresh in its mind.

Oklahoma probably never would have seen Route 66 had it not been for Cyrus Stevens Avery, Tulsa oilman, restaurateur and auto fanatic. Back in the early days when cars were indulgences and auto clubs were hobbies, many roads were little more than trails blazed and marked by auto clubs. But, Cyrus Stevens Avery took automobiles seriously. He was so vigorous in his promotion of roads he was named in 1922 as the first chairman of the state's new three-member highway commission. The U.S. Secretary of Agriculture, who was then responsible for such things on a national level named him a consulting highway specialist to sort the tangle of state roads, county roads, backwoods roads and auto club trails into some kind of a linkup that would become the nation's first trans-continental highway.

Avery – who owned a famous hotel and restaurant just outside of Tulsa – convinced everybody it was in the best interests of the nation to turn the proposed road from the traditional northern route along the old Santa Fe trail and bend it to the south so that it joined the old California Gold Road. It just happened to pass on that new route through Avery's hometown of Tulsa, and on through flourishing Oklahoma City on its way west. All the pieces had been put together and Route 66 was completed and made passable and christened in 1926, in time to become the main highway out for Okies fleeing Oklahoma's deepening dust and depression in the thirties. It came to be known as the Main Street of America. And there, in the pride of its very inception, lay the seeds of its demise.

The trucks that trundled down the main street of America kept getting bigger, faster, more frequent and more dangerous. The trucking industry was emerging as a competitor with the railroads for moving transcontinental freight. Oklahoma City was becoming a trucking hub for the nation. The business communities of Oklahoma City and Tulsa were coming to see the possibilities. As business grew, romance faded.

By the middle 40s, the Mother Road was showing its age. It wobbled through Sapulpa's main street. Bristow. All the little towns in Lincoln County. Ninety-degree turns all the way through them. All the stop lights. Davenport. Through Stroud, then Chandler, then Jones. It would take thirty minutes to get through Edmond. A motorist got to Oklahoma City about four hours after leaving Tulsa if he drove fast and had good luck with stop lights. And the world was moving faster than that.

In 1947, Governor Roy J. Turner proposed an idea new to Oklahoma: let the people who wanted to get from Tulsa to

Oklahoma City in two hours instead of four pay for the road that would make it possible. Those who did not want to pay could take the old romantic road that dawdled down the main streets of all the little towns. Roy Turner was a natural leader, he had been a success in the oil business. He had been president of the school board in Oklahoma City. People listened to Roy J. Turner.

On coming into office, Turner had reorganized the highway commission and named H.E. Bailey to head it. And, when the turnpike talk started, Turner also named Bailey to supervise the new Oklahoma Turnpike Authority which the Oklahoma Legislature authorized in 1949. Bailey became the day-to-day driver in a campaign to build a super tollway between Oklahoma City and Tulsa.

One of the first men Turner named to the new turnpike authority was R.P. Matthews, editor of the *Sapulpa Herald*, and a good guy. He was so enthusiastic about the new road that Turner named him chairman. Engineers got busy designing, acquiring right of way. Matthews then made it known he wanted only one thing from all his work as chairman of the Turnpike Authority. He wanted the turnpike to go down the mainstreet of Sapulpa, where all of his merchants would get the business.

"That defeats the purpose of the thing!"

Everybody tried to talk to him.

"That's why we are building the turnpike, Mr. Matthews, to get a road directly from Oklahoma City to Tulsa, without stopping at lights."

When Matthews realized he was presiding over an agency that was going to move traffic away from the doorsteps of his hometown merchants, he resigned to became a leader of the anti-turnpike movement in Oklahoma. And the battle lines were sharply drawn.

All the towns on Highway 66 were against it with good reason. Turnpikes have little access. Almost a wall up. Isolating traffic and zooming it unseeing past their little tourist courts and restaurants.

Bailey was getting all the co-authors he could. He approached the new kid from the country that he had helped with his highway workers. Asked him to become a co-author of the turnpike bills.

Gene liked the idea immediately. Roads to be paid for directly by the people who use them was the only new thing people were talking about.

There were turnpikes already, Ohio, Pennsylvania, New Jersey. Texas was building the Dallas-Fort Worth turnpike. Most of the Eastern states had them. They worked. Paid for themselves and then some.

Ground was broken for Oklahoma's turnpike under Governor Turner's direction, then his term ran out.

From about '48 on, the gambling and drinking sat ever more uneasily on Wade. He had read the Bible from a kid up. His daddy was a self-made student of the Bible. Had always taken the family to Sunday School unless he had hay down in the field and it looked like it was going to rain. Wade would get to thinking about all that. Jesus. Reading about Jesus. About loving them that hates you, doing good to them that despitefully use you, praying for them that curse you. Loving your enemies. Wade would get to studying on those things, and he couldn't quit, and it really would get on his nerves. He had done some things that sure hadn't ought to have been done, and he had almost done some things that were worse than that.

There was a time back in Eufaula when an old boy put a knife to Wade's neck and took five dollars away from him in a dice game. That old boy was just as wrong as he could be. Wade had gone to Kirksey Nix to talk about it.

"Well, Wade, I'm not going to tell you it's alright to kill him, but if you've got to do it, do it the way I tell you and I can get you out of it."

Kirksey, was just a young lawyer then, first year out of law school.

"Are you sure he will pull his knife, Wade?"

"Yeah, he's a knife man. He'll pull his knife."

"Well, when he pulls his knife, you go to backing up. Get yourself into a hemmed up place. You'd a run if you'd a had a chance to, but you were hemmed up and couldn't run. This is the way I will get you out of this."

"Okay, Kirksey, that's what I'll do."

"Wade?"

"Yeah, Kirksey?"

"Before you get all hemmed up, make sure that gun will fire."

Wade had gone to a friend and borrowed a gun and the two of them had carried it down on the creek. And it had fired just fine. Wade had set out to find the knife man. And he had done just as Kirksey had told him.

"You took five dollars away from me with that knife, but you'll never take another nickel."

The man ran his hand into his pocket and came out with his knife.

Wade started backing up into the corner a fence formed with a building. Got himself totally cornered so there was no way out. Then he came out with the pistol. Aimed it. Stiffened his finger on the trigger. Then that Jesus stuff started up in his head about not killing anybody. About praying for those that despitefully use you.

"Throw down that knife!"

The man did.

"Do good unto them that..."

Disgusted, Wade walked up to the man and got the knife and stepped on it and broke the blade off and threw it at him.

"Don't never try that no more."

Wade had thrown the warning back over his shoulder as he walked away. Shaking his head. Wondering.

"How in the world I gon love a man like that? How I gon love my enemy with him puttin' a knife on me! How could that happen? You heaping fire on me, and I must speak kindly and this stuff?"

And that was always the point at which Wade stopped studying it over and hunted up Billy Ray or Onegone or Shirt or somebody and they had them some drinks and got into a card game, and Wade forgot about it. For a while.

1950 President Truman ordered the first Air Force and Navy units to Korea after Communist troops poured over the line drawn between North and South Korea in the settlement of World War II. He sent 35 military advisers to South Vietnam and agreed to provide military and economic aid to the anti-Communist government there.

In the United States, country folk were going to town, and the niceties of town were going to the country. Since 1933, the percentage of families working the land had dropped from 25 per cent to ten. Three fourths of those who stayed on the farm now had electricity. Sales of television sets boomed in city and country alike. More than 100 stations were broadcasting in 38 states, and one American in four owned an automobile.

Firefighters found a badly burned little black bear cub clinging to a charred tree trunk in New Mexico's Lincoln National Forest. They took him down gently and flew him to Santa Fe where a game warden took him home and nursed him back to health. He was so engaging a little fellow he was shipped to the National Zoo at Washington, D.C., where he captured the nation's heart and became the symbol of forest fire prevention. His name was Smokey the Bear.

20

Eyes of a Startled Hawk

Johnston Murray – lawyer son of old Bill Murray – won a narrow Democratic primary election runoff over William O. Coe in the 1950 race to succeed Roy J. Turner as governor of the State of Oklahoma. Murray led by 960 votes out of 470,700 cast. Coe demanded the first statewide recount in Oklahoma's short history. To watch the recount for him in Pittsburg and McIntosh counties, Murray hired a young lawyer from McAlester who was just completing his first term in the House of Representatives.

Wade stuck with his old friend Bill Coe. From that night in Ada back in 1946 when he had fished in his pocket and donated $2 to Coe's first campaign against Turner, Wade had this gambler's intuition that if he stayed with that $2 bet he would win someday with Coe. Wade was in a better position to help than he had been in 1946. He now was worshipful master of the Negro Masonic Lodge in Ada, and he threw all the lodge's 71 votes behind Coe. And he stood late in the back of his old pickup truck in countless black communities across Oklahoma, urging Negroes to go with Coe, veteran of World War II.

"Bill Coe over in a foreign country smellin' gunpowder while Johnston Murray layin' up over here smellin' talcum powder."

Turned out Phil Ferguson, former Democratic congressional candidate from Woodward was the real war hero in that election. He contended that neither Coe nor Murray ever heard a shot fired in anger, and the only powder Coe smelled was talcum, too. Ferguson ran fourth in the four-man primary. The recount changed only 19 votes. Coe was out again. And so was Wade. Murray went on to win the governor's office over Republican Jo Ferguson, 329,308 to 313,205.

In those days of Oklahoma politics, the governor had the power to appoint the leadership of the Senate and the House. Murray, impressed by the relaxed young McAlester lawyer, named him assistant majority floor leader, and Gene, 23, suddenly was third-ranking House member, below only Speaker James Bullard and the majority floor leader as he began his second term in the House. Taken somewhat aback – he hadn't even voted for Murray – Gene kind of looked off out the window when he told J.I. Easygoing as he was, J.I. hadn't forgotten Johnston's old daddy yanking him off the picket line and putting him in prison for the night back in 1932.

Strolling into the governor's office one day, Gene met a man who impressed him as no other ever had.

"Now, Johnny," he was saying, "there isn't anybody who can ride that old political horse. You know that. I'm going to run for the Corporation Commission one of these days, and I don't want to commit political suicide. We've had four governors since 1936 and seven welfare directors. The answer is no."

The two looked up when Gene walked in.

He was a tall man, spare, with piercing blue eyes and a severely disciplined shock of hair. He had on cowboy boots. A white cowboy hat lay on the edge of the governor's desk. His right shoulder drooped slightly.

"Hello, Gene," said Murray. "Meet the man who is going to run the welfare department for me."

He had, the governor said, driven his old daddy all over Western Oklahoma back in 1930. Now a storekeeper, successful originator of the Binger Trading Company, he had been one of five coordinators for Johnston Murray's campaign for governor.

The man's eyes were compelling. Had in them the look of a hawk, startled into watchfulness. He extended his hand.

"Lloyd Rader," he said.

Gene liked him. Really liked him. Trusted him from the instant the two hands came together. The eyes met straight on.

Murray interrupted.

"Lloyd, I've got a speech coming up in Michigan, some kind of a conference on aging. Will you at least go do that for me while I get things organized here?"

"Well, Johnny," the man grinned. "We can talk about that."

"Daddy! Daddy!"

Slowly, Wade roused to consciousness. Somebody was tugging at his knee.

"Let's go home. Let's go home, Dad."

It was his daughter, Carolyn. Wade didn't know where he was or why Carolyn was tugging at him. He sat quiet and studied on it. It was night. Both of his little girls were there. The lights were on. He was sitting on a church pew. Slowly, he put it together in his head. The Christmas program!

Wade had done some drinking that Christmas Eve with his friends, but he had gone home as he had promised so he could go to church with the girls and watch them perform in their little Christmas play. He could remember leaving the house.

"Hey, Wade!"

As the three of them walked to the church. It was Billy Ray.

"Have a drink with me, ol' Wade."

"Can't, Billy Ray, already had enough."

"Don't you do that to me, Wade. This is Christmas."

And he had had one just so Billy Ray would leave him alone. And then he had had another. And then he had come up the stairs to the Methodist Church and sat down in front where his daughters could look right out there and see him watching their little play. And then he must have passed out. Drunk. Before the program even started. Slept through it all. Preacher must have left the lights on so he wouldn't wake up there in the dark. Alone. Except for his two little girls.

"Daddy, please! Let's go home."

Wade struggled to his feet. It was heavy on his mind all night.

Sunday morning was Christmas. He went to church with his family. Bad as he felt. Much as he hated to face that preacher. And the preacher told about how Joseph kept going from hotel to hotel, motel to motel, trying to find a place for Mary to have the baby Jesus. How nobody would let them in.

"We got people right now, and we got them sitting up in this church this morning, won't allow Jesus a place to be born in their heart."

And he looked straight at Wade.

21

Case of a Slain Wastebasket

Johnston Murray was a big man. Tall and broad-shouldered. But, unlike his father, he was a shy man. His greatest strength was that in the first hour you heard him talk, you were convinced he could do anything. It made him one of Oklahoma's better speakers, and the combination of that and his charm and his last name was what had made him the 14th governor of the State of Oklahoma. But what happened after that first hour worried his supporters. Or, what didn't happen. Johnston Murray loved most to doodle. Play with little games.

You could walk into his office with the weightiest of legislative problems and Johnston Murray would be sitting at his desk fooling with a new puzzle or something. Or he had a cartoon he had to show you before he wanted to hear what your problem was – which often was his problem you were coming to let him know that he had. He lacked leadership in the legislature. He could think up good programs, and then they would just lie there or they would be defeated because nobody was throwing the power of the governor's office behind them. At Gene's urging, regular meetings were scheduled between legislative leaders and the governor to try to get some of the legislation moving. Gene learned quickly that he needed all the help he could get.

There were three guys who probably were the greatest orators in the history of Oklahoma. Kirksey Nix, who had moved to McAlester and became one of its two state representative was one of them, but, he had switched over to the Senate in 1950. The ones who stayed in the House were Frank Grayson, who had served two terms in the late 30s and early 40s before being elected again in 1950, and J.D. McCarty, against whom Bob Bates had made his unsuccessful run in 1948.

As Johnston Murray's assistant floor leader, one of Gene's jobs was to get Murray's programs through the House, although he would admit privately he had to hold his nose to bring up some of them. Gene would take the floor, and the old veterans would take after him, and it felt like being fed to a peanut thresher. Then Johnston's floor leader was called into active military duty, and Gene was left pretty well alone with them. He would watch those old guys huddle and then look at him and grin. He knew what they were saying: "What are we going to do to that kid today?"

One especially troubling morning Gene went down early to talk with the governor before anybody else got there. A lot of the newer members, including himself, were upset that lobbyists for big companies wrote most of the bills for the legislators, and they wrote them to suit the companies who hired them. There was a young guy named Stewart Strasner at the University of Oklahoma whom Gene wanted to hire to come up and write bills for the House members the way the members wanted them written. Gene's mind was buzzing with ideas, and he was eager to talk.

There was that year a brand new novelty. It was a pistol-shaped cigarette lighter that lit when you pulled the trigger. Everybody was wanting one of them, and anyone who knew the governor knew he would have one. And there he sat. No matter how hard Gene tried to talk with him about the legislative program, Johnston kept playing with that pistol. He would point it at the lamp, point it at Gene, sight down its barrel, just as if it were a real gun. But he never would pull the trigger.

"Governor, I don't mean to offend, but we have got to talk about this legislative program."

Gene said it as if it was the last ham of winter. Governor Murray pointed the pistol at the big metal wastebasket. Sighted carefully down the barrel. And, finally, he pulled the trigger. But it didn't light.

The explosion nearly stopped Gene's heart. Acrid gunpowder smoke curled toward the ceiling. When the wastebasket quit spinning, it had a neat hole near its middle. Murray laid down the pistol.

"Okay, Gene what do you want to talk about?"

"Damnation, Governor! I thought that was a cigarette lighter!"

"No," he said, "I haven't got one of those yet."

Joe Barrow was the Negro son of a sharecropper from Lexington, Alabama. Long before Jackie Robinson was cracking the racial barrier with a baseball bat, Joe Barrow – fenced off from the real world in a boxing ring – was being cheered for whipping white boys with his fists. By 1936, he had dropped the name Barrow picked up his middle name and had become Joe Louis, the Brown Bomber. He took away the championship that Jimmy Braddock had worked so hard to wrest from Max Baer in the fight they still talked about on Peaceable Mountain. And then in 1938, Louis successfully defended his title against the German Max Schmeling, and a miracle happened. The whole free world stood up to cheer a Negro sharecropper's boy who had knocked a white boy unconscious with his fists. Now, there had been a Negro heavyweight boxing champion before Joe Louis. His name was Jack Johnson and he became champion in 1908, but the white folks never had liked him. His ascension to the title had split the nation. Set off race riots. The miracle of Joe Louis was that in their excitement over his whipping Schmeling, Americans forgot, for a moment, that Joe Louis was black. He was a fighter, he was a gentleman, and he was a man.

Louis retired in 1949 after holding the world heavyweight boxing championship longer than any other living human. He lost a comeback bid in 1949 against Ezzard Charles, but that didn't hurt too bad because Charles, too, was black. Then, in 1951, Joe Louis, the hope of the black world, was knocked out by white Rocky Marciano in a defeat that ended the Brown Bomber's career. Closed out a dream. With humiliation.

Wade heard the news on the road. Traveling the north of the United States by bus, hunting work. Wade went to studying on it and how angry that would have made him before that Christmas week when he had passed out in the church.

Somewhere out between Milwaukee and Chicago, a white boy got on the bus, and that bus was crowded. One seat there and it was right beside Wade. The white boy wouldn't sit down in it. Stood there. Must a rode that way a hundred miles. He put his hands on the luggage rack and balanced. Stood on one foot a while and the other foot a while. Wade scooted away in his seat, far as he could, giving him plenty of room if he wanted to sit down. Finally, that white boy come and sat down on the arm of the empty seat. Turned his back to Wade. Wade studied his back for a long time.

"Mister," Wade said finally, "have you got a cigarette?"

Wade didn't smoke.

That white boy turned around and handed him a cigarette, but he turned his back right back around. He rode that way for three or four miles. Wade reached out and touched him.

"I hate to be bothersome, but have you got a match?"

He gave Wade a match. Turned his back again.

"Did you hear the fight?"

Wade said it to the white boy's back. He could see him stiffen.

"Man," Wade said, "that Rocky Marciano is one of the best fighters ever come out, I guess."

That white boy turned to face Wade, then, and he went to talking about Rocky Marciano. He was, he said, his hero. And Wade finally figured out if Negro boys needed so bad to have heroes like Joe Louis, then white boys must need some heroes. Wade and the white boy still were talking about Rocky Marciano when it came time for him to get off. The white boy started for the opening doors of the bus then stopped and turned back.

"I'm glad I met you," he said.

He put out his hand.

"Doggone."

Wade said it to the darkness after the doors had closed.

For its first century, higher education in the United States was confined to a few universities, church sponsored, or related, and little thought had been given to the plain, everyday people who worked for a living. In 1862, Congress passed the Morrill Land-Grant Act providing funds to start U.S. land-grant colleges for the scientific education of farmers and mechanics. And by the time Oklahoma Territory came into being, higher education had come to be recognized as a public responsibility, not a perk for the well-to-do. So, when Oklahoma and Indian territories were told to prepare for statehood, they were told to prepare to provide higher education for the general public.

There developed three kinds of public education: education for the business and professionals; education for farmers, mechanics, the working people, and education to train teachers to teach in the rural schools and the elementary and secondary schools of the territory.

There developed three schools with which to do it: University of Oklahoma in Norman for business and professionals; Oklahoma A&M College in Stillwater for working folks; Central State Normal School in Edmond for teachers.

(A college for Negroes was established at Langston in 1897 with a goal of teaching Negro boys to be good farmers.)

And that crucial period is where E.T. Dunlap started research for his new doctoral dissertation after everything kind of ganged up on him in 1951 and forced him to junk his first dissertation on how he reorganized the state's common schools so that a school bus ran within walking distance of every high school student in the state.

He still was superintendent of schools at Red Oak, was in his third term as a state legislator, and was getting ready to resign and run for state superintendent of schools so he could see that his new Common School Code was implemented correctly in Oklahoma, as he had seen that Buffalo Valley High School was set up properly.

Then the office of president of Eastern State College at Wilburton became open. E.T. was offered the job but turned it down. He had work to do, he explained, in common education. Then his personal hero called him in. Dr. Henry Bennett, president of Oklahoma A&M told E.T. he should take the job as president of Eastern State College. Higher education, he said, needed him. Then Senator Robert S. Kerr called. Then Dr. W.B. Bizzell, president of the University of Oklahoma.

"Anybody can be state superintendent of schools," they told him.

❖

In December of that year, after giving one of his brightest students his last bit of good advice, Dr. Henry Bennett died.

The man who was born in a log cabin over around Hope, Arkansas, died 65 years later when the airplane in which he and his wife were traveling the world slammed into a mountain peak in the

Elburz Mountains of Iran. He was doing what he had always done, learning and then passing that learning on to others so they could live better lives.

"I have lost a friend," said President Truman, "and the American people have lost a great teacher."

"He was," said Senator Bob Kerr, "a dreamer of no small dreams."

All Gene knew was that plane crash killed Dr. Bennett a long time before he was through doing all the things he would have done for the world. But, he sure lived long enough to be hero to a boy from Peaceable Mountain. And the taste of oranges and apples came back into his memory. And their Christmas odor was bittersweet.

But Gene never did remember the year 1951 as the year Dr. Henry Bennett died. Or even the year Johnston Murray killed his wastebasket, or made him a leader in the legislature. There was a piece of legislation passed that year, authored by young Representative George Nigh from McAlester, the significant section of which read:

"Whereas, Agnes Stipe, wife of our beloved Assistant Floor Leader Gene Stipe, did on March 1, 1951, present to said Gene Stipe a bouncing baby girl weighing nine pounds and three ounces, christened Mary Elizabeth..."

22

Reaching into a Snakepit

Somewhere off in the gloom, Hayden Donahue could hear someone vomiting. He could understand the vomiting because he had seen the food, but he could not see the person who was sick. Thick iron bars and filth on the windows shut out the bright, sunny day that was going on outside. He waited as the big, dismal room came slowly into view, and he could make out an old woman crouched on her heels in a far corner of the room. So many beds were lined up so close he could see no way to walk across the floor to her from where he stood at the door. He got hold of the nearest bed rail, hoisted himself onto the bed and walked the length of the room, stepping bed to bed, placing his feet carefully so he did not step on the upturned faces of any of the pitiful old women lying there. Thus battle-hardened Dr. Hayden Hackney Donahue got his first really good look at the responsibility he had agreed to assume. Even he was appalled.

The stories reporter Mike Gorman had written after the bishop's horrifying visit to Central State Hospital in Norman in

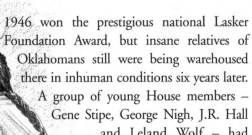

1946 won the prestigious national Lasker Foundation Award, but insane relatives of Oklahomans still were being warehoused there in inhuman conditions six years later. A group of young House members – Gene Stipe, George Nigh, J.R. Hall and Leland Wolf – had decided to do something about it, but they hadn't known what. So, they had set out to find someone who did.

They came across this guy down in Austin, Texas, who had impeccable credentials. He had worked with some of the top names in the business and had received national honors for his innovations. At age 40, he was assistant director of institutions for the State of Texas.

Gene nudged George Nigh.

"Look at that," he said.

"What?"

"There, Pittsburg, Oklahoma. Pittsburg County."

"What does that have to do with anything?"

"He's a Pittsburg County boy, George, grew up ten miles south of Peaceable Mountain. I'll bet I can talk to him."

In autumn of 1945, General Omar Bradley, who had heard much about Grinker's brilliant psychiatry student, had moved Donahue to the Veterans Administration Central Office in Washington to help design new hospital programs for a generation of badly damaged young men. When Donahue had completed that assignment, he had asked to be named acting manager of the VA hospital in North Little Rock, Ark., while he figured out what he wanted to do with what remained of his life. He married Patricia Toothaker of San Antonio, Texas, and started a family. In 1948, Donahue resigned from the VA and began a partnership with a new psychiatrist with a new goal. George Jackson was the new superintendent of the Arkansas State Hospital, and he was determined to bring it into the 20th century. The two formed a team: Jackson would deal with the political problems, Donahue would run the programs. Their efforts in Arkansas earned them citations of merit from the American Psychiatric Association and an offer to run the Texas Department of Institutions which included five mental hospitals and other facilities ranging from institutions for the blind and deaf and tubercular to an Indian reservation. But their plans for progress kept running aground on political patronage. And that was where the young legislators caught up with the Oklahoma boy from south of Peaceable Mountain.

Donahue turned out to be a wonderful little guy with a lopsided grin, and he looked out at the world through popbottle glasses. He was a dreamer – until they started talking business, then he was blunt. Gene would shift him off to talking about how he had grown up ten miles south of Peaceable Mountain in a coal mine town, and how his daddy, too, had got in trouble organizing workingmen, and Donahue finally told Gene he would try to help Oklahoma, but only as a consultant. He was swamped, he said, with the work of setting up a cerebral palsy unit on Galveston Island in Texas.

Donahue visited Oklahoma and sat down with the young legislators and Stewart Strasner, whom Gene had managed to hire as a bill-drafter. Donahue put a psychiatrist's dream on paper. The mental health department would be governed by a seven-member board appointed by the governor and confirmed by the Senate – with staggered terms so no governor ever could control it. Then he went wistfully home to try to complete his cerebral palsy unit on Galveston Island.

Before the bill he had helped draft could even be passed, the Oklahomans were back, asking Donahue to move his family to Oklahoma and implement the dream. We want you to revolutionize the state's mental health care system, they said. The names behind the offer were impressive. Governor Johnston Murray, Senate President Pro Tem Raymond Gary, Speaker of the House Jim Nance, and a young guy named Gene who had grown up on Peaceable Mountain just north of his old hometown. And that is how the nationally known Dr. Hayden Hackney Donahue, who never really seemed to have control of his own career, ended up kneeling in the corner of a filthy room, ministering to a sick woman in Central State Hospital in Norman, Oklahoma.

He found only four toilets for the 150 people housed in the unit. One bathtub. No wonder it smelled. The bars on the windows were to him a monument to superstitious ignorance, not of safety. The only people in the building were decrepit old women. It was a fitting end to a day that had shaken Hayden Donahue to his shoe soles. Even after seeing patients in Arkansas fed oatmeal and coffee in the same bowl, after treating terror-palsied soldiers within earshot of the bloody guns of war, Dr. Hayden Donahue was sickened by what he saw in Central State Hospital in America's heartland. This was the system of care and treatment of the mentally ill that he had agreed to take over.

It was going to take a long time and a lot of help to hack Oklahoma out of this wilderness. He had read of the grand opening of a new superhighway – the Turner Turnpike – that cut driving time from Tulsa to Oklahoma City from four hours to two and brought Oklahoma into the forefront of modern motoring. And he turned sadly back into the darkened room.

Wade's wife died of cancer. She was 26 years old. Wade's oldest girls, Carolyn and Diana, had been joined by Ensi, Lincoln, and Larry. Wade took a job selling insurance. He let his late wife's mother keep the kids in Ada and paid her $150 a month. Welfare paid the rest. Wade bought his first car that year, a 1934 model Ford two-seater with doors that opened from the front. He began to spend most of his time in McAlester, but he wasn't gambling. From the day that preacher had looked right at him and told him how people wouldn't give little Jesus a place to be born in their hearts, he had not gambled and had not drunk. Hadn't gone after anybody with a chair leg or a knife or a gun. He tried to explain to the baffled Onegone and Billy Ray and Shirt.

"I was the shamedest fella that you ever saw in your life, and I could see then that I had some straightening up to do."

Lloyd Rader wore his cowboy hat and boots to his new job of trying to ride the old political horse known as the Oklahoma Department of Welfare. It was a political appointment, he knew, that could not last, and he had agreed to try it out of deference to the shy and needy son of old Alfalfa Bill Murray. But when he sat down in the director's chair and started rummaging through the papers, he saw some things that those who had gone before him had not seen.

Congress had authorized the U.S. Department of Agriculture to buy surplus wheat, butter, cheese, dry skim milk, vegetable oils, and other surplus foods for donation abroad or to sell abroad. The idea was to help relieve world hunger and put a prop under U.S. farm prices. Kind of a twist on Roosevelt's cattle killing. Lloyd Rader began to hound the U.S. Department of Agriculture.

"Let's give it to Oklahoma people who don't have the money to buy it and let them eat it," he insisted. "Now."

It made sense. The market-sogging surplus became groceries on the tables of needy Oklahomans. State institutions began to get the free food. Welfare Director Lloyd Rader became the distributor, and that right there was the real beginning of America's commodity distribution program. It worked so well in Oklahoma, it got to be a model program for the nation. Like Dr. Henry Bennett and the Agricultural Extension Service, Mr. Rader did not invent it, but he made it work. And that was when he took off his cowboy hat and boots and put on his business suit and decided he would stay for a while.

Gene liked to go over and talk of little things like how Mr. Rader had spent some time with Alfalfa Bill Murray's shy young son when he was shepherding the old man around western Oklahoma, and how he had introduced him to a beautiful, red-haired girl named Willie Emerson, and how she became the state's beautiful, red-haired first lady named Willie Murray. And then he knew why this storekeeper from Binger could call the governor of Oklahoma Johnny.

From time to time, Gene would break into the small talk: "Mr. Rader? What do you think about building one of these commodity distribution warehouses in McAlester? We sure could use the work."

Lloyd Rader decided he just might be able to work with this young man.

1954 *A 19-year-old kid named Elvis Presley achieved moderate success with recordings of "That's All Right, Mama" and "Blue Moon of Kentucky," gasoline cost 29¢ a gallon, and computers were used for the first time by American businesses. Evidence emerged that smoking is hazardous to health.*

The Supreme Court ruled that racial segregation in public schools was unconstitutional and ordered states to proceed "with all deliberate speed" to end it. President Eisenhower refused to help French troops surrounded at Dienbienphu, and South Vietnam defeated them and gained independence from France. Senator Joseph McCarthy charged Communist spies permeated the U.S. Army.

Pittsburgh, Pa., school children received the first mass poliomyelitis immunization shots, and Harvard physicians performed the world's first successful kidney transplant.

23

How Do You Campaign Against Red Foley?

Hayden Donahue removed the heavy iron bars from windows that separated helpless old women from the world. He painted dismal doors. Set about revolutionizing the mental health system in Oklahoma as he could with what he had to work with. But, as he improved the old buildings, there was this idea that kept growing in his head. It had started on the bloody battlefields of North Africa.

He and Grinker had raised the remission rate of soldiers suffering from combat stress by 43 percent over what it was in World War I. With proper drug use, why wouldn't treatment centers in or near the communities where people got sick and to which they would return have the same advantages as the treatment tents near enough to combat to remember how it was? That, Donahue decided, was the answer to Oklahoma's mental health needs.

When he started looking around for staff enough to man the community health centers, he remembered something else he and Grinker had done in South Africa. When there were not enough mental health professionals to go around, they had gone to other professions and sold them on the idea of mental health. Got the general practitioners to give mental health services.

"Mental illness doesn't start when you're old," he told everybody who would listen, "it starts when you're very young. First- and second-grade teachers should make more money than college professors. They are the ones that really bend the kids."

Dr. Donahue began marathon trips to visit every medical community in the state to try to get all aspects of the medical field interested in and oriented to mental health.

Gene's admiration for the gentle little psychiatrist grew as their association closened. Donahue wanted the legislative committee to go around and see what the other states were doing. They learned there were only two doing anything. Huey "the Kingfish" Long, much-maligned dictatorial governor and U.S. senator had made Louisiana first in the nation with modern treatment centers that tended the wage earner at night and the housewife by day. New York had copied them.

Finally, the legislature passed the bill Donahue had helped draft. It increased the department's budget by $1 million, bringing it to $7 million. He initiated a four-year resident-training program to lure young doctors, and Central State, the hospital that had shamed a nation, became one of the first to use drugs in treatment of schizophrenics.

Donahue hired 40 nurses and such "exotic" professionals as occupational, music, and recreational therapists. He set up a 240-hour training program for the aides and an additional 160 hours for supervisors, and established psychological testing to help ensure that the employees weren't victimizing the patients with their own psychopathologies.

Another pioneering physician, Dr. Stewart Wolf, became chairman of the Department of Medicine at the University of Oklahoma. He and Donahue arranged for residents to staff a medicine and surgery clinic at Central State. Together, Donahue and OU also established a nursing program and an internship program for psychologists and social workers.

Donahue began a psychiatric residency program and hired former student Dr. Harold Whitten to run it. They were able to recruit several top residents and staff psychiatrists almost immediately because Donahue knew what the younger people in the field wanted, and he offered it. Everybody wanted to be an analyst, so Donahue hired Dr. Hugh Galbraith, trained at the Chicago Institute and a faculty member at Menninger Foundation in Topeka, Kansas. Galbraith would teach and provide analysis to any interested resident or staff physician. There were 110 applicants for seven first-year residency positions. Donahue worked endlessly.

He established a children's ward, and he rounded up the 500 tubercular patients and isolated and treated them. A new law made abuse of patients a crime. He stopped prefrontal lobotomies and punitive electro-shock treatments and started a professionally organized and operated food service program.

Patient mortality declined by 27 per cent; for the first time in history, more patients were discharged than were admitted. Many were sent to be with families who had volunteered to care for them. Donahue also began working state and national sources for the money to develop his community treatment programs.

Donahue allied himself with colleagues in other states to persuade the National Institute of Mental Health and Congress to fund a national community mental health movement.

Then he saw a glimmer of light. The job was monumental, but not impossible. People actually were listening to him. But, then, Dr. Donahue – gentle, soft-spoken, with a definite air of the country boy about him – was easy to hear.

In the summer of 1954, it looked like Wade finally had him a winner in the governor's race. William O. Coe was making his third try for governor, and Wade was back out campaigning all the black towns. The front-runner was State Senator Raymond Dancel Gary, former president pro tempore of the Senate. And it made for a hard summer for Wade.

Roscoe Dunjee's *The Black Dispatch* had done everything but endorse Gary. Said despite the fact that he came from Madill, deep in Little Dixie, blacks had no reason to fear the powerful state Senate leader who began his public career as a school-teacher. Said the schoolteachers had come down on the side of the blacks in the integration question. And that Gary was a non-drinking, non-smoking, Bible-believing Baptist. But Wade just couldn't bring himself to give up on that $2 he had laid on Bill Coe.

Everybody who had ever thought about getting into a political race did in 1954. Fourteen Democrats. Five Republicans, although no Republican in history had been elected governor of Oklahoma. The first black man in state history – on the Democratic ticket. Outgoing Governor Johnston Murray's pretty, red-headed wife, Willie, got in. So many got in Wade had to watch himself to keep from campaigning somebody who was running for office. Campaigning got so hot and dirty that Johnston Murray borrowed a page from his old daddy and called out the National Guard to watch polling places in Sequoyah, Adair, Pittsburg, LeFlore and Cherokee counties on primary election day. It was a hot, blistery Oklahoma day when anything could happen. And it did.

William O. Coe beat Raymond Gary 159,122 to 156,376 to win the Democratic primary election for governor of the State of Oklahoma, and it looked like Wade might not have to sell insurance any more. He was ecstatic. After all these years! Bill Coe would not offer him a nigger job. All Coe had to do was keep low and get through the runoff election with Gary, and Wade's life would take a definite turn for the better. Then it happened. Wade couldn't believe it.

"Doggone.

"I guess," he explained to his friends, "Bill Coe was just so power-drunk and happy about winning that primary that he started to attacking everything and everybody."

"They say I'm going to fire the warden at the penitentiary," Coe would say, "and I am. I'm going to fire him."

And Wade would wince. And Coe would say, "When I take office, that's a signal for that bunch over there at the state capitol to get out."

Wade would writhe in frustration.

"There goes 8,000 votes, right there!"

Then Coe jumped on Harry Bailey who had cut driving time between Oklahoma City and Tulsa from four hours to two, and was busy getting ready for another turnpike that would extend superhighway driving all the way from Oklahoma City to Joplin, Missouri. Harry Bailey had some millionaire friends – Bob Kerr, the Phillips family – and that smoked all of them out with all of their money, and they all went after Coe. Finally, Coe lost his temper and went after Raymond Gary with his fists in front of the television cameras and had to be pulled off by his own people. Raymond Gary beat Bill Coe 251,920 to 233,079 in the runoff election of 1954, and Wade was out of it again.

Incumbent U.S. Senator Robert S. Kerr survived a squeaker that year. Former Governor Roy J. Turner, for whom the state's first turnpike was named, gathered 205,241 votes in the primary election to 238,543 for Senator Kerr. With nine men in the running, it forced Senator Kerr into what could have been a scary runoff election. But, having run out of money and out of heart for the thing, Turner dropped out before the runoff and went back to his oil and cattle, clearing the way for Kerr to continue the writing of his American legend.

Wade did have one winner that year. It was Kirksey Nix. Wade helped him campaign against a young state representative from Pittsburg County who bet an incredibly successful beginning in the

House of Representatives that he could win Nix's Pittsburg County state Senate seat.

Kirksey had challenged U.S. Representative Carl Albert for the Third District seat in Congress in the off-year in 1952, and even though Albert beat him 45,941 - 23,259, the fact that Nix had challenged him angered some folks in Pittsburg County whose daddies had mined coal alongside the Albert boy's daddy, Ernest. Gene Stipe was one of those folks. The Nix-Stipe race was hard-fought and close. So close Kirksey finally called in a famous friend, singer Red Foley, who toured the McAlester-Pittsburg County area singing gospel songs for Nix's campaign. The Stipe boy shrugged when it was over.

"How do you campaign against Red Foley?" he said.

And he went to his office over Webb's typewriter shop to practice law. And read in the newspapers what was going on out in the world. And in Oklahoma City.

One of the people he read about was Kirksey Nix. And he would lean back in his chair and laugh. He couldn't help it. Kirksey Nix was good.

One of the issues Kirksey had kept hammering in the 1954 election in which Representative Stipe was retired to the private practice of law was the open range. Under that law, cattle could graze freely on unfenced land in rural areas, and motorists attempting to make their way down the highway had the responsibility of dodging them. Kirksey had come out strong for a law that would require the cattle to be under fence. Gene had said little about it one way or the other, but Kirksey had waxed eloquent as only Kirksey could about the dangers to pregnant women and little children of racing down the highway at 60 miles an hour and suddenly confronting a herd of cows lying in the road, absorbing the last heat from the day's sun.

"We've got to fence out these cows to make our highways safe for our people!"

That and Red Foley had kept him in the state Senate.

But, when the bill to require fencing in of livestock came up in the Senate, the gallery was full of big-hat boys with cowboy boots on and denim, glowering down upon the seated senators – especially Senator Nix. Kirksey took the podium to speak for his bill. Surveyed the gallery for a long and discomfiting time. Then he grinned.

"Now, gentlemen," he said, "What we've got to do is fence off these dangerous highways to protect our cows from these motorists."

And the faces in the gallery reddened for a different reason as a roar of involuntary laughter swept the gallery amid sounds of cowboy hats slapping knees and cowboy boots stamping the gallery floor. And the cowmen learned what Gene already knew. You couldn't get too mad at Kirksey Nix. Even when he beat you.

24

The Preacher's fur-Trimmed Wife

Gene was leaning back in his office one bright summer day, contemplating an empty appointments calendar and the pleasant walk just completed from his rented house to work, necessitated by not yet having made enough money as a practicing attorney to buy a car. The secretary he shared with his partner, Guy Andrews, came in and handed him a business card. The name, but not the title, jumped at him from out of his past: "The Rev. M. Clyde Pedersen."

"He is in the waiting room" the secretary said.

The only Clyde Pedersen Gene could remember was a friendly, good-looking kid at Savanna High School. Big, tall, gangly. But that Clyde Pedersen was adept at doing those things that made people call a boy ornery when he really wasn't. He would do stuff like talking the boys into playing hooky. Clyde had almost got Gene and the other boys in his class expelled when he started a crap game down at the outdoor toilet and talked them into playing. Clyde may or may not have made it all the way through high school, Gene couldn't remember, because when World War II started, everybody had got into such a rush to enlist that some of them did as soon as they graduated and some before they graduated, and a bunch of them were lost to memory in the confusion. First thing Gene knew, he had looked around for Clyde and Clyde had gone off to war. After the war was over and everybody was back, they got to asking what ever happened to old Clyde Pedersen. No one knew, except, somehow, the rumor got out that Clyde was preaching. Everybody laughed.

"That boy is in prison somewhere."

Even at the class reunions, everybody asked about Clyde, and nobody had heard a word about him except for this rumor that he was preaching. And now, Gene held proof of it in his hand.

"Faith and Healing," the card said, was the Rev. M. Clyde Pedersen's business.

"Show him in," Gene told his secretary.

The Rev. Clyde Pedersen had on a new suit, necktie with a big diamond stickpin, diamond rings. He and Gene visited a while, and then Clyde wanted to take Gene down and show him his Cadillac and his wife. His wife was all in fancy clothes, had on a big fur coat. M. Clyde Pedersen was a clear picture of success and prosperity.

He had a tent, he said, that would seat five hundred. Had his own 500 chairs. Had his own truck to move the chairs. He was on his way to Houston to conduct an outdoor revival. Thought he'd drop by. The two of them had a nice visit, and the Rev. M. Clyde Pedersen got into his Cadillac beside his fur-trimmed wife, and they drove away to Houston, and Gene walked back upstairs to contemplate his empty office and appointments calendar and the nice walk he had had to work that morning from his rented home. And, perhaps, the efficacy of earning one's way to prosperity in some easier manner than as a practicing attorney and fledgling politician.

Gene was restless. It was like coming back from the excitement of the war. Things he had helped to start were going on in

Oklahoma City without him. Hayden Donahue was revolutionizing the care of the mentally ill, and it was drawing the attention of the nation. Lloyd Rader had reorganized the entire welfare department. Harry Bailey was clearing the way for another turnpike, the Will Rogers. Legislation for it had been completed while Johnston Murray was in office and Gene was a legislative leader.

Gene was fascinated by turnpikes and the revenue bonds that financed them. During slack hours with no clients, he read. Turnpike financing, he learned, was a replication of how they built the old barge canals, the Erie Canal. They were paid for by fees paid when barges went up and down those canals. Most of the early bridges were built as toll bridges, especially in Indian Territory. One of the earliest ways the civilized Indians learned to get cash money from the white man was to build bridges and ferries across the many streams in Indian Territory and levy a fee for crossing. At one time, nearly all the bridges that existed in the country were toll bridges, and some still were in 1954. In the case of revenue bonds, money is simply put up in advance against the prospect of fees that will be paid when the highway or canal or whatever, is put into use.

By 1955, many Oklahomans had decided they liked turnpikes, but by then they had a governor who didn't. Raymond Dancel Gary liked free roads. He had campaigned on a pledge to provide a $250-million, five-year road-building plan to add more than 2,000 miles to the state system. Free roads. No tolls.

There was a lot of pressure to build the second turnpike. The Turner had made money from the day it opened, and now had enough history for it to be known it was going to be a success. This second turnpike would give motorists and truckdrivers a straight shot from Oklahoma City to Missouri. Nobody could be sure what the traffic volume would be, so the only way the bond market would underwrite the bonds was that Oklahoma pledge revenues from the Turner to pay off the Will Rogers.

Governor Gary finally agreed that if the people approved it, he wouldn't fight it. Sixty three percent of the voters in the special election voted to cross-pledge. Once cross pledging was established, it became much easier to build turnpikes.

Harry Bailey had more on his mind than cross-pledging. In addition to wanting to build big projects, he wanted, finally, to make him some decent money. The bonding people demanded that there be a consulting engineer and that the engineer be affiliated with a nationally recognized engineering firm that had credibility with Wall Street. H.E. Bailey withdrew as director of the Turnpike System and worked it out so his friend and understudy, Bill Hoback, replaced him. H.E. struck a deal with the nationally recognized engineering firm that had done the Turner Turnpike, and Oklahoma's Mr. Highway became the consulting engineer for all the turnpikes that would follow.

And all those things were going on in Oklahoma City, and Gene was in McAlester, sitting in his office above Webb's Typewriter shop.

It was along in the afternoon, three, four o'clock, months later when the collect call came from the Carter County Sheriff's office.

"Uh, who did you say again?"

"The Rev. M. Clyde Pedersen."

"Clyde?"

"They've got me in jail down here, Gene."

Gene got into the used car he had managed to scrimp enough money together to buy, and he drove to Ardmore and bailed the Rev. Pedersen out of the Carter County jail. Clyde had a sister living in McAlester, and he said he would ride back with Gene and stay the night with her. On the way back, he told the story of how he came to be in the Carter County jail and without his fur-trimmed wife or his Cadillac.

The Lord, he said, had continued to bless his work, but Clyde admitted he had got to paying more attention to a girl gospel singer than he was to his wife, and one thing led to another, and Clyde and his wife got a divorce. That fur-trimmed wife, he explained, had been George and Matt Kimes' niece. They were notorious bank robbers. The Kimes brothers' sister was Clyde's ex-wife's mother, and she was married to the kingpin bootlegger in Ardmore. Clyde had come through Ardmore with his car and truck and tent and chairs and so forth on his way to Texas to hold another revival, and he had decided to stop off to see his kids. But, for some time, Clyde had been overlooking paying his child support. So, the county's law enforcement immediately went into full swing, and they arrested Clyde, impounded his Cadillac, truck, tent, chairs and everything and put him in jail because of his failure to pay child support. Gene kept noticing that Clyde still had on his diamond rings and fancy suit.

"Clyde, I sure aim to represent you and do you a good job and try to get you out of this mess, but you've prospered and done well. I want you to know that I'm just struggling, and you are going to have to pay me some kind of a fee."

"Well, don't worry, Gene, I plan on doing that. The Lord will provide. Don't you worry."

The Lord had proved he would take care of Clyde, but he hadn't been all that quick about showing he would cause Gene to prosper. It was good, at least, to hear Clyde was planning to pay. Gene took him by his sister's house, and told him to keep in touch and he would go to work and try to get him out of this mess. Gene and Agnes went to J.I. and Rosie's house the following Sunday for dinner.

"Joe, do you remember old Clyde Pedersen you went to school with?"

"Yeah, Dad, I remember him."

"He's in some kind of trouble."

Gene looked off out the window like he did when J.I. heard he was Johnston Murray's assistant floor leader.

"Really?"

"Clyde's preaching down here at the little church, holding a revival, and they took up two collections, one for the church and one to pay Clyde's lawyer."

That was the best news Gene had heard in a while, but he wasn't about to tell J.I. Stipe that the lawyer Clyde was taking up the collection for was his son. Gene kept waiting for Clyde to bring in the proceeds of the offering. Gene began to get a little discouraged about Clyde's fidelity to his obligation to his lawyer. He went back for dinner with J. I. the following Sunday.

"Joe, this thing about Clyde Pedersen is really odd. They've had a revival going down there ever since he got here. I went down there with Rosie last night and they took up an offering for the church and one for his lawyer, and then Clyde called them together, and said the piano was out of tune, and it was a disgrace to have a piano out of tune in the Lord's house like that.

"'We can get it tuned by a professional piano tuner for twenty-five dollars. I realize ya'll have been good about contributing to the work, but I want to take up a special offering to get the piano tuned.'

"So they had a big prayer and passed the plate around and only had $13.

"So, Clyde got back up there.

"'We've got to try a little harder. I told you there's no way we can get a professional piano tuner to tune this piano for less than twenty-five dollars, so let's try real hard and see if we can't raise that much.'

"They took a fourth offering, but everybody who had any money had given it, and they ended up with nineteen dollars and something.

"'You've all been wonderful,' Clyde told them. 'You've done your very best, but there's no way we can get a professional piano tuner to tune this piano for less than twenty-five dollars. I'll tell you what I'm going to do. I'm going to take the nineteen dollars and tune it myself.'

"And he put that $19 in his pocket and walked back and sat down to hear the last of the singing."

Finally, Clyde showed up at Gene's office with some of the collection money, and, thus blessed, Gene worked out a deal with Carter County to get back Clyde's Cadillac and truck and 500 chairs so he could go back to making money to pay child support to his fur-trimmed former wife. Gene advised Clyde – as any good attorney would do – to keep current with his child support payments to the niece of George and Matt Kimes and the stepdaughter of Carter County's kingpin bootlegger. Especially if he planned any more visits to Carter County. Last Gene heard of him, the Rev. M. Clyde Pedersen was back on the highway to a successful career in the ministry.

Two big things happened in Wade's life. He remarried, and he accepted pastorship of a church. The church was down at Wilburton. It wasn't anything to support him and let him give up selling insurance or make him give up politics or anything, just a chance to preach what he had learned: that if you tried real hard you could kind of live, sometimes, the way Jesus said to. All that love-them-that-hate-you, and pray-for-people-who-was-doing-bad-things-to-you stuff, he would tell his new parishioners, it do work. But not easily. Wade only had to drive down to Wilburton every other Sunday because that was as often as the congregation felt it could afford to pay a pastor. It was, as they say, one of those every-other-Sunday churches.

25

A Defense Lawyer Spurned

In 1956, there was an election for judge of the Oklahoma Court of Criminal Appeals that Oklahomans still talk about in much the same way as Pittsburg Countians still talk about that famous "mule man" race for the state Senate in the 1930s. But the story of how the court race came to be started a long time before 1956. Wade was in on it from the start. Let him tell it.

This all started back there in 1953.

We had a fellow by the name of Carl Austin DeWolf. He was sentenced to death for killing a police officer in Tulsa by the name of Jerry Sinclair on August 30th of 1946. Kirksey had this case the reason I know so much about it. Kirksey went to his grave believing DeWolf was innocent, and doggone if he ain't got me believing DeWolf was innocent.

Me and Kirksey went out there to the penitentiary to see DeWolf, and Kirksey, he asked DeWolf, he said, "Carl, where was you August 30th of 1946?"

DeWolf said, "Kirksey, where was you last year, August 30th ?"

Kirksey couldn't tell him. So we talked there with him a while, and we went home. In about a week, Kirksey called me, and he said he had talked to DeWolf again and DeWolf had said he believed he could tell Kirksey where he was that night.

"He said he was in a little old town they called Cushing. Said he stayed at a hotel there with a girl they called Big Red."

Me and Kirksey, we talked about that two or three days and Kirksey, finally he said, "Wade, let's run over there and see."

Me and him we left and went to Cushing, and we went to this hotel. He found one of the black boys there was a porter and he asked him if he knew a girl there they called Big Red. The boy said yes.

"Will you get her for me?"

About thirty minutes, he had Big Red there. So Kirksey, he asked Big Red if she know Carl Austin DeWolf. She said no.

"He said he stayed all night with you here once. August 30th, 1946."

She still couldn't remember, and Kirksey he asked the hotel manager, he said, "Have you got any records on who stayed here that night?"

"Yeah, they up in the attic, but I can go up there and dig them out."

Kirksey said he'd appreciate it, so he went up there and dug it out. Now Carl Austin DeWolf was from Springfield, Mass., and they had a name there, that was Carl Williams from Springfield, Mass., had stayed there that night. Kirksey asked them to bring Big Red back. And he asked if she knew a Carl Williams and she said she remembered that name.

And she said she remembered that he give her a two-dollar tip. Kirksey asked DeWolf when we got back, said, "Did you give her a tip?"

"Yeah."

"How much?"

"Two dollars."

"Do you know a fella called Carl Williams?"

"Yeah."

"Who is that?"

"That's my father-in-law."

"Did you ever use his name any?"

"Yeah, sometimes I'd check into hotels and motels and that kind of stuff, I'd use his name."

You know, they wouldn't let Kirksey enter that into court. They just said the trial was over. Carl Austin DeWolf was sentenced to death. Then they'd do this kind of talk:

"Well, by God, he might be innocent, but he was a thug, anyhow."

They executed him. Man that hurt Kirksey. Well, it hurt me, too. I hate to see a man I believe was innocent go down.

In 1956, Dick Jones was acting as presiding judge of the Court of Criminal Appeals for the seventh time in his seventeen years on the bench. He had been appointed at age 34, youngest man ever to serve on that court. Jones had personally written 1,130 opinions, including 99 murder cases and eighteen death penalty cases, an average of forty more per year than the national average of appellate judges in the United States. Judge Jones was proud of his record, and he made it the focus of his campaign when he came up for re-election. But there was one case in there that he probably should have left unmentioned.

Pittsburg County State Senator Kirksey Nix was serving his fourteenth year in the Oklahoma Legislature. He was engaged in the private practice of criminal and civil law and had handled 45 capital cases, purportedly more than any other 42-year-old lawyer in the country.

Carl Austin DeWolf brought the two men together. He was executed on Nov. 17, 1953, after nine stays of execution – and after Court of Criminal Appeals Justice Dick Jones had said DeWolf should have no more stays from Governor Murray. Kirksey Nix raised all kinds of oratorical hell.

On June 22, 1955, Kirksey Nix was found guilty of three counts of professional misconduct, including "falsely, willfully, and maliciously" attacking the integrity of the Court of Criminal Appeals and the individual judges; using his official position as a state senator in an attempt to obstruct the due administration of justice in the DeWolf case and utilizing political pressure to unduly influence the courts and criticizing the court on television.

And that is when it became significant that Dick Jones, nationally ranked Court of Criminal Appeals judge, was up for re-election in 1956. Pittsburg County's Senator Kirksey Nix announced he would oppose him.

In his office over Webb's Typewriter shop in McAlester, former state Representative Gene Stipe read Nix's decision in the newspaper. He put it down, and walked out of his office to go visit with some folks.

About that time, Gene met this black fellow who sold insurance in McAlester. Furniture, sometimes. He was a colorful man. Part-time preacher down at Wilburton. Ex-gambler. His name was Wade Watts. Gene had known of him for some time, but had never really become personally acquainted with him. Knew he had campaigned the Negro community for Kirksey when Gene ran against him for the state Senate back in 1954. Wade and his little brother, Buddy, had become good speakers. Good enough that people would drive miles to a political campaign they were not personally interested in just to hear them debate. Gene had first met Kirksey when he moved to McAlester to practice law with George Hill. In addition to being an eloquent speaker and quite a good lawyer, Kirksey had a great feeling for people, their rights. Gene liked that in a man, whatever else people said about them. Some people are limited. Have a difficult time surviving in a competitive world. And they need somebody there to defend them just because they need to be defended. And you usually would find Kirksey Nix there doing that. But Gene had other reasons, also, for hoping Kirksey Nix upset veteran Appeals Court Judge Dick Jones in that 1956 race for the Court of Criminal Appeals. A man couldn't be a judge in Oklahoma City and a state senator from Pittsburg County at the same time. Gene dropped by to meet the colorful, preaching ex-gambler. The Negro, Wade Watts.

26

A Conservative Little Dixie Integrationist

Marshall County, Oklahoma, is so deep in Oklahoma's Little Dixie it bumps Texas. Peanut country. Oil country. Old-time cotton plantation country. Bill Murray country. It was created at statehood from Pickens County in the old Chickasaw Nation and named Marshall because George Henshaw of Madill was the constitutional convention delegate representing the area, and he loved his mother and wanted her maiden name printed somewhere forever. The county seat is Madill. It was named for a St. Louis attorney for the railroad.

A farm kid named Raymond Dancel Gary was born out between Madill and Kingston in January of 1908, two months after Oklahoma became a state. Raymond grew into a Southern Baptist conservative school teacher. Superintendent of schools. He sold books and school supplies and dabbled in the oil business, sort of looking around for a place. In 1941, he ran for the Oklahoma State Senate and won, and he found his place. Raymond Dancel Gary was a politician – in office or out – from that day until the day that he died. A patient man, he spent the next 14 years working his way up through the Senate from freshman to chairman of appropriations committee, majority floor leader and president pro tempore, collecting power and knowledge of state government as he went. By the time he had ducked Bill Coe's flying fists to become Oklahoma's 15th governor in 1955 there was not a whole lot about state government Raymond Gary didn't know.

When it came time to obey the United States Supreme Court's order to let Negro children go to the same schools as the white kids, everybody kind of looked out of the corners of their eyes to see what this Little Dixie Southern Baptist Democrat from Bill Murray Country would do. Raymond Dancel Gary quietly set in motion the legislative machinery to kill legislation growing out of old Bill Murray's constitution that set up the special fund to educate black children separately. Without money to operate black schools, local school districts couldn't afford segregation even if they wanted it. So they had to send the little black children to white schools. Bright yellow school buses had to stop and let them get on. Thus it was that in the Oklahoma countryside, legal separation of school children by race died with hardly a whimper. At the hands of a southern Baptist conservative Democrat from Little Dixie.

"As an active Baptist and believer in the Scriptures," Gary said, "I have never understood how persons can call themselves Christians and believe that God made them superior because they were born with white skin."

And he lived his Christianity so quietly that few people even realized what he had done until they started studying the history of how Oklahoma ended its system of racial separation so peacefully. Well, most of Oklahoma.

❖

"Doggone."

Wade laid aside the newspaper. Things were forcing him to take a closer look at his personal politics. It was disconcerting that the little black kid who had to step off the old dying-rose-colored dirt road to make way for the school bus carrying the white children had grown up to oppose Raymond Dancel Gary to the last bitter vote. In favor of old Bill Coe. And then Raymond Gary had been the one to end racial school segregation in rural Oklahoma. And even Bill Murray's own son who had been in the last year of his term when the order came down, had said, quite simply: "Our people have demonstrated that whatever the law is, it will be accepted."

And Wade had fought Johnston hard.

("Bill Coe over in a foreign country smellin' gunpowder...")

Going with old Bill Coe against all of them.

"Doggone."

Over in Arkansas, Governor Orval Faubus had called out the National Guard to prevent black students from entering all-white Central High School in Little Rock. Faubus caved in before a federal court order, but not until he had stirred up hate in Little Rock so bad that when the little black children entered the school, they had to be taken out again for fear their white neighbors would hurt them. President Eisenhower had to send in armed federal troops to protect the little black children from the white people they had grown up with.

"Doggone."

Wade began walking the streets of McAlester. Visited every business in town. Walked in the front door of the hotel where he was not permitted to eat or stay overnight.

"Well, Rev. Watts, I have absolutely nothing against Negroes, but if I let them come in here, that'll just ruin my trade."

"Well, what if everybody else let them come in?"

"Well, I will too, then."

And then Wade walked next door. Schoolteacher Lloyd Porter wanted desperately to help him, to be a part of it, but he had been threatened with firing if he agitated, so he rode with Wade. Stayed in the car. Wade would ask for the manager of whatever establishment he visited.

"Well, Rev. Watts, I have absolutely nothing against Negroes, but…"

Until he had visited every motel, every café. And everybody said if everybody else let Negroes come in, then they would, too. Except this little joint down on Chickasaw Street.

This one guy heard what Wade was doing, and he called him on the telephone and cussed him out and told him no niggers were coming in his place including Wade, so Wade didn't try to integrate the café. It was a joint that wasn't fit for kids and things to go in anyway, so Wade figured the Negroes be better off if they couldn't go in that place. After walking out the town, Wade called a city-wide meeting. And he told them as friendly as he could: "The kids all going to go to school together, now. We know that. The Supreme Court done said it, and we know this has got to happen."

And the people of McAlester agreed, so Wade went to work on the kids. He wanted to get them acquainted with each other before they walked into those classrooms together for the first time. He started calling regular meetings of the youth of McAlester at the town's community center. He would gather about 150 white kids and maybe 50 or 60 black kids and get all of them together and all of them would have a big time. Everything went smooth and friendly until the night the adults were meeting at the community center and Wade had to move the gathering of kids to the Catholic Church gymnasium. Everybody had a fine time there as they had at the community center. But at about 11 o'clock when all the kids were getting home, Wade's phone went to ringing. People calling to cuss him out. White folks didn't mind their kids mixing with Negroes, and Negroes didn't mind their kids mixing with whites, but both of them were furious with Wade for taking their kids into a Catholic Church.

"Doggone."

Something else that didn't make headlines was that when Governor Raymond Gary went into his new office and started unpacking boxes and looking for what to do first, there was a knock on his door; it was a group of legislators.

"Raymond," they said, "Johnston Murray did at least one thing right. We feel like Lloyd Rader should stay over there as head of the welfare department."

And something about the way they said it, Raymond Gary – who would become one of the most powerful governors in Oklahoma history – chose not to disagree. And Lloyd Rader was off to another round of riding that horse he said nobody could ride.

In 1957, the Soviet Union, flagship of world communism, launched Sputnik I, mankind's first Earth satellite, and followed it quickly with another that carried a live dog into orbit. The Will Rogers Turnpike between Tulsa and the Missouri state line was opened to traffic, and J.I. Stipe's blackheaded boy, Gene, was sworn in for his first term as the new state senator from Pittsburg County.

It hadn't really been a difficult race at all. Kirksey had defeated Dick Jones for the seat on the Court of Criminal Appeals, vacating the seat he had defeated Gene to retain in 1954. A special election was called to fill Kirksey's Pittsburg County Senate seat, and Gene had won it. One of his opponents was his friend, Lonnie Brown, and the other was a long-time acquaintance and former foe, C. Plowboy Edwards, who was becoming Gene's friend. Wade, who had helped Kirksey win, joined with Gene in his race to replace him as state senator. Gene got the feeling they, too, were going to be friends for a while.

It felt good to be back at work. Gene teamed up with state Senator Ray Fine of Gore who had served in the state Senate since 1953, and, they handled a most unusual bill, at least for two politicians from the backwoods. Here is how it came about: One of the first things Robert S. Kerr had done when he won that U.S. Senate seat in 1948 was to go into the leadership of the U.S. Senate and arrange to have himself assigned to the Rivers and Harbors Subcommittee. By 1955, he was that subcommittee's chairman, and in 1956, appropriations for the Arkansas River Navigation project had tripled. And there was a reason for that. Senator Kerr won funds for three of the 13 reservoirs vital to the navigation project in return for throwing his rapidly growing political clout to the popular Federal Aid Highway Act which authorized the interstate highway system.

Congress passed the highways act and President Dwight D. Eisenhower signed it into law. A far cry from the piecing together of paths and dirt roads to make old Route 66, the law authorized construction of a 42,500-mile network of roads to link major U.S. urban centers, with 90 percent of the $33.5 billion cost to be borne by the federal government. Wonderful program for Oklahoma. But there was a problem.

In addition to the 10 per cent that would be their share, Oklahoma had a statute that required every city to pay for relocating utilities within the city limits on any highway project. Inside the limits of Oklahoma City, the highway would cross hundreds of sewer lines and water lines, and Oklahoma City could not afford its share, and more of the Interstate money was to be spent in Oklahoma City and Tulsa than the rest of the state put together, and any super roads passing through Oklahoma to connect major urban centers would pass through Oklahoma City. So the project was dead in the water in Oklahoma. Governor Gary, who loved free roads, wanted the highway construction desperately. Being a country boy himself, he naturally went to the country boys for help.

Gene and Ray Fine handled a bill to provide that the state would pay for relocation of those utilities critical for Oklahoma City and Tulsa. The two of them chuckled about it.

"A coupla country boys looking after the big cities."

They got the Oklahoma highway system off high center. The first project was Interstate-35 that bisected Oklahoma from border to border and connected Oklahoma City with Dallas to the south and Wichita to the north and eventually tied in with most of the major cities of the nation. And the four-lane super road was free from border to border in Oklahoma. It was so much what Raymond Gary stood for that they decided to name the road the Raymond Gary Expressway. Put a big sign out there. And that pleased Gary immensely. He so wanted to be remembered as a governor who did good things for Oklahoma.

During his last month in office, Raymond Gary made a final call to Mr. Rader, who had proved to be a most congenial political partner, to tie the ribbon around his tenure in the state capitol. Gary explained to Mr. Rader that he wanted a quick welfare increase so the record would show the folks how much welfare folks were getting when he came in, and how much more they were getting when he left. Let the next governor worry about how to pay for it. Then he learned one of the reasons why Mr. Rader could stay when lesser men could not.

"Can't do it, governor. I didn't spend all the money when you were coming in, and I can't do it to anyone else."

The governor, unaccustomed as he was to being told no, called Rupert Jones down at Antlers. Rupert was chairman of the Welfare Commission that ostensibly governed Mr. Rader's department.

"If that is the way Mr. Rader says it is going to be," Jones told him, "that is the way it is going to be."

Governor Gary was furious. Governors had done it historically. He was, after all, only trying to follow precedent. But that was before Lloyd Rader mounted that old political horse.

27

The 90 Days of Cannonball Joe

In the waning days of the 1958 gubernatorial primary election in Oklahoma, fiery young J. Howard Edmondson, former county attorney from Tulsa, had pulled close to the leader, Midwest City building millionaire Bill Atkinson, but he couldn't quite close the gap. Atkinson, a conservative Democrat and a school-teacher who had made his money selling real estate at night and on weekends, had the endorsement of outgoing conservative governor Raymond Gary. Edmondson, at age 32, was the antithesis of everything conservative, and he was bringing it head-on to the old-time rural bloc that had run the state for so long. He would, he vowed, throw out the Old Guard. Every last one of them. And Bill Atkinson, he said, was the anointed heir of the conservative Old Guard. And J. Howard Edmondson fanned that into a campaign so hot, and his oratory was so fiery, and his hair was so flaming red that his campaign came to be known as the Big Red Prairie Fire. But he couldn't quite get the edge on conservative Bill Atkinson.

Searching for a tender spot, Whit Pate, Poteau attorney and avid Edmondson supporter, paid a man to take a card around Poteau with boxes to check off on what was most on people's minds. And then Whit Pate took the results to J. Howard Edmondson. Just about everybody had checked prohibition. Whatever else was on their minds, prohibition was, too. Bible-thumpers or bootleggers, it was the one thing they wanted to make their feelings known about, for or against. The ban on liquor had been put into the Oklahoma Constitution at statehood primarily because of the Indians, and been kept there because of Oklahoma's alleged opposition to the consumption of alcohol.

J. Howard had supported repeal of prohibition all along, but now he saw a way through his stalemate with Bill Atkinson. By promising to get it on the ballot quickly so everybody could have their say, he could draw support from both sides. The last bit of advertising cash was squeezed from supporters.

In 1958, everybody knew that you had to have the newspapers behind you to get elected in Oklahoma. But there was no time for a newspaper campaign. Gambling, Edmondson spent the money on a series of television spots. At their cheapest, in mid-afternoon. And the handsome, eloquent young redhead hit television sets in living rooms all across the state, promising Oklahomans – including a heavy percentage of housewives – a vote on repeal of prohibition within months of his election to office. And the old political pros could feel the gears shift. Deep down where there is leverage.

J. Howard Edmondson edged Bill Atkinson in the primary by 108,358 to 107,616, less than a thousand votes, sending the two into a runoff election. And the prairie fire was raging unchecked. Over in Bill Atkinson's headquarters in the Huckins Hotel, supporters went desperately scrambling for loose votes for the runoff.

Wade's perennial candidate, William O. Coe, had pulled 72,763 votes to finish fourth. The decision was reached that the only way Atkinson could win in the runoff was to get Bill Coe's people. Senator Gene Stipe – who was as close to a manager as there was in the Bill Atkinson campaign – went after them. He convinced Clarence Redden, Coe's campaign manager and Charlie Fuller, co-manager, to throw in with them. Moved desks for them into Atkinson headquarters. Got them on the phones, trying to switch Coe voters, raise money. Sat there for a moment, listening to them at their work. And couldn't believe what he heard. In a matter of minutes, he heard Charlie Fuller promise two different guys they could be Eighth District highway commissioner if they would support Bill Atkinson.

"Charlie," he said, "we need to have lunch."

One thing Atkinson was adamant about. He wanted to be a governor who hadn't promised anybody anything.

"Charlie, you're going to be in deep trouble with Bill Atkinson. I heard you promise both those guys they could be Eighth District highway commissioner."

"Doesn't make any difference," Charlie shrugged, "We aren't going to win anyway."

And he went back to his cheeseburger.

And J. Howard Edmondson swamped the Midwest City millionaire 363,742 to 158,780 in the runoff election and became the youngest governor in Oklahoma's history. He was 33 when he was sworn in. And before he even was sworn into office, he had changed the face of politics in Oklahoma forever. That shift everybody felt when he passed Atkinson, also meant that the day of newspaper dominance in political campaigns was gone. It, too, had gone over to a relative newcomer – television.

One of Edmondson's first acts was to send workers out to Interstate 35 and tear down the signs that said it was the Raymond Gary Expressway. And it was a hurtful thing for a man who wanted desperately to be remembered for the good he had done for Oklahoma.

Edmondson set about immediately to consolidate his appeal to young voters. He took up the cause for the cities against the Old-Guard rural interests. Surrounded himself with young men dubbed "the crewcuts." And immediately ran headon into a dilemma. A group of legislators came in for a visit that was becoming an Oklahoma tradition.

"Mr. Rader," they said, "stays."

Lloyd Rader had been discovered by Alfalfa Bill Murray, hired by Johnston Murray and retained by Raymond Gary, and there was no way Edmondson could separate him from the Old Guard. Rader went down to see the new governor with his obligatory offer to resign.

"Lloyd," said Edmondson, "I don't think you should continue as welfare director."

"I serve at the pleasure of the welfare commission and not the governor," Rader reminded him, " but the job would be intolerable if the governor didn't want me."

And it looked like that old horse had thrown him. But, as Mr. Rader prepared to pack for his return to his trading post at Binger, J. Howard came across a dilemma within his dilemma. Edmondson's bill to put prohibition on the ballot ran aground in a legislature he had just defied.

Reluctantly, he called Lloyd Rader.

And it was discovered, amazingly, that the young governor did have enough votes to get prohibition of repeal on the ballot. And there was no more talk of Lloyd Rader leaving.

Gene watched the Fort Worth taxicab thread through traffic to the curb. He jumped in, eager to get his business completed and get back to Oklahoma. But the cab sat there for a moment. At the curb.

"Hello, Gene."

He looked at the driver.

"Johnston? Johnston Murray! What in the hell are you doing driving a taxi?"

"Well," said the man who once shot the waste basket in the governor's office, "I'm trying to make a living."

❖

In the Oklahoma of 1959, a clear choice whether to allow drinking or not to allow drinking was not to be had under existing conditions. There were enough bootleggers and illegal drinking clubs in Oklahoma to keep the drinkers and partygoers happily sopped while the Southern Baptists and temperance leaders could claim a dry state. Everybody was a little bit happy about it, but nobody but the bootlegger, perhaps, was totally happy about it.

Somebody decided to make the upcoming election a true vote on whether there would be recreational alcohol in Oklahoma or whether it would be truly dry. Joe Cannon, an Edmondson friend and young Muskogee County lawyer, was chosen to make Oklahoma face the truth.

"Howard named me commissioner of public safety, head of the Highway Patrol, and he put the crime bureau under me," Joe said, "He couldn't (legally) name me to both jobs, but he gave me the Crime Bureau. You needed an army to do it."

From January through March, 1959, Joe rode at the head of the Midnight Raiders in an old black Cadillac left behind by Governor Gary. He set up roadblocks at state borders to intercept liquor deliveries and conducted highly publicized raids of private clubs for the well-to-do that previously had been exempt from the law. The passion with which he did it threw such fear into local police that they began to raid and close hospitality rooms at business and social conventions. Joe called in airplanes, stopped and searched trucks on the highway, and picked up the nickname "Dracula" by asking that all auto accident fatalities be given posthumous blood tests to determine if they had been drinking. When sheriffs refused to accept confiscated whisky, Joe stacked it up on their porches for the public to see. Diehard drinkers toasted Cannon bitterly with special "Cannonball cocktails" which were made of weak beer served in champagne glasses. It went on for 90 days. Then Oklahoma went to the polls, and 396,845 voted to repeal prohibition, and 314,480 voted to keep it, and Oklahoma was wet at last. At least moist. Sales of liquor by the drink still were forbidden.

It was Edmondson's most remembered feat as governor, although he instituted the Merit System that removed thousands of Oklahoma employees from political patronage and Central Purchasing which removed political favoritism from buying of state supplies. Joe Cannon went into history books as the night-riding raider who did what nobody had been able to do in decades of trying.

"It was," he said of his history-making feat, "fun."

"We can't have a former governor of the State of Oklahoma driving a taxicab in Fort Worth, Texas," Gene told Whit Pate. "It isn't right. Doesn't look good."

Gene had opened a law office in Oklahoma City and Whit Pate had moved up there after Edmondson was elected, and the two of them had sort of thrown in together.

"I have this account, a trucking company, that is going into Mexico, and they need a lawyer who can speak Spanish, and Johnston lived in Bolivia when his dad was trying to establish a colony down there. Johnston is very fluent in Spanish."

So it was, Gene talked his partner into hiring former governor Johnston Murray, who had given him his start in the leadership of the House of Representatives. And Gene took Johnston out of the taxicab and put him into a Cadillac. Gave up his own office and moved over into a little cubbyhole.

"He was our governor," Gene told Whit, "I want him to look good."

But Johnston Murray still loved to doodle, and he still was as strong as you get … during the first hour. Gene soon was set to remembering the hole in the wastebasket and the frustration of getting Johnston Murray to settle down to business. The trucking company account got so scrambled even Gene couldn't undo it, and he quietly picked up the phone and called Mr. Rader. Johnston Murray, former governor, worked quietly as an attorney in Mr. Rader's welfare department until he died.

❖

Back in the early '50s, about the time Hayden Hackney Donahue was being persuaded to take over Oklahoma's disgraceful mental health system, two Montreal, Canada, physicians reported success in treating psychotic patients with an anti-vomiting drug they had obtained from France. By the middle 1950s, the Federal Food and Drug Administration had approved its use in the United States under the trade name thorazine. It looked like a miracle. Patients who had been psychotic for years were being freed of crippling hallucinations and delusions after a week or so of thorazine treatment. Dr. Donahue was ecstatic.

Although not a cure, and not universal in its effectiveness, the new drug became one of Donahue's strongest allies in his fight for the Community Mental Health Centers. Mentally ill patients could be treated with maintenance doses of thorazine administered in their own hometowns.

Psychiatrists all across the nation began jumping on the bandwagon. The next step was convincing Congress to provide matching funds to establish a nationwide system of community mental health centers. Witnesses appearing before Congress were a who's who of American psychiatry: Dr. Jack Ewald, departmental chair at Harvard and personal friend of U.S. Senator John F. Kennedy of Boston; Dr. Dan Blaine, medical director of the American Psychiatric Association – and a bespectacled country kid from south of Peaceable Mountain called Hayden Donahue. And it looked like they were going to win the community mental health center battle. Thousands of patients already had been discharged or were eligible for release. Success was near and appeared inevitable. But Hayden Donahue was losing his war in Oklahoma.

"After a time," he said, " the legislature gets to looking at you and says, 'We got you straightened out. Now it's education's turn or somebody else's.' Consequently, I hadn't been getting the funding I needed to upgrade the staffs and buildings at Eastern and Western State hospitals."

In his seven years in Oklahoma, Donahue's record had been impeccable. He had received several top administrative awards from the American Psychiatric Association, reformed Oklahoma's snake pits, crisscrossed the state to educate the public – even when he knew only a handful of ordinary citizens would attend his presentations. But, Donahue was getting the feeling he was coming to be regarded by many as a man who was biting the hand that had fed him. Some Oklahoma lawmakers who had fought hard for him in his efforts to reform Central State Hospital could not understand why he now wanted to start tearing it down. Sending its patients out into centers scattered across the state. Sending many of them home.

Dr. Hayden Donahue resigned. Didn't whine or complain. Didn't gripe about the legislature. He just quit. Moved his family back to Little Rock. Went back to complete the residency training in psychiatry that had been interrupted by the Japanese bombing of Pearl Harbor, and to serve as clinical associate professor of psychiatry at the University of Arkansas School of Medicine. Help teach others to carry on with what he had been doing in Oklahoma.

28

Never Walk into a Dog Fight

In 1961, a guy named Yuri Alekseyevich Gagarin became the first human being to ride a rocket off the earth and into space. He was a Russian, and Russia was Communist, and that proved, the Russians said, that communism was the future of the world. But Yuri Gagarin also did something Russia didn't intend for him to do. His flight kicked in the afterburner on the American educational revolution that started in 1957 when Russia orbited its Sputnik rocket with a dog aboard.

Dr. M.A. Nash, Oklahoma's first and only chancellor of higher education announced that he would retire in July of 1961 and let some younger blood handle the revolution. And that is when an Oklahoma mountain kid named for the prophet Elijah and his daddy Lum's twin brother Tom was yanked right into the middle of everything. Ten years after listening to his hero Dr. Bennett and accepting the presidency of Eastern Oklahoma A&M College in Wilburton, E.T. Dunlap was quietly reaping the rewards of having brought the school into the new age, just as he had done with common education.

But after six to eight months of looking around and interviewing and finding nobody suitable to be the new chancellor, somebody finally made the connection and invited E.T. Dunlap to apply to become the number one man in higher education in all of Oklahoma. It would be a formidable assignment for two primary reasons:

War babies conceived almost two decades before were reaching college age, promising a deluge of college students to surpass even the boom in 1946 when their daddies came home from the war.

Two, knowledge was exploding as U.S. research institutions desperately sought to equip American education to compete with the successes of the totalitarian form of government as represented by the USSR.

After mention of E.T. Dunlap's name, a clamor arose for him to accept the chancellorship, but E.T. was reluctant. There was a third problem. An Oklahoma problem.

Governor J. Howard Edmondson was in his early 30s. George Nigh, who was swept into the lieutenant governor's office by the Edmondson prairie fire was just getting into the 30s. Governor Edmondson's "crew cuts" were abroad in the land. Everything in the executive branch was youth and new ways of doing things.

J.D. McCarty of south Oklahoma City, one of the most powerful legislators in Oklahoma history was speaker of the House. He had been in the legislature since 1941; Everett Collins, of Sapulpa, was president pro tempore of the Senate. He had been in the Senate since 1947. So everything in the legislative branch was the old way of doing things.

The governor and his "crew cuts" wanted the Old Guard out, and the Old Guard controlled the Legislature with an iron hand. The thing E.T. Dunlap wanted least was to be caught in the middle. E.T., as any adroit politician could see, had friends on both sides of this question, and E.T. wanted to stay with his friends.

Five regents of higher education got together and called him and asked him to meet with them. He did, and they offered him the job. Backing away, E.T. tried to explain:

"Now you older regents that I have worked with for ten years as college president, that's fine."

But, there had been two unplanned vacancies on the Board of Regents for Higher Education, and, despite the best efforts of those who drew up the plans for the Oklahoma higher educational system, young J. Howard Edmondson was going to end up with a voting majority on the board when and if his choices for their replacements were approved.

"These old boys that he's fussing with in the legislature are good friends of mine," E.T. continued. "I served with them. I believe in the philosophy of the governor, but as chancellor I could not be effective as executive officer without the support of the state regents, and I wouldn't have that complete support without the friendship of the governor and the legislature together. I cannot take the job unless I can get these people all together and know that I am going to have the united support of all."

In November of 1960, latter part of the month, E.T. got a call from the governor's executive assistant, H.I. Hinds, a friend, also, of E.T.'s, who had served in the legislature as speaker and was a key player for the governor and U.S. Senator Robert S. Kerr and the like. Hinds said Governor Edmondson would like to have a visit with him, and would he come up to the mansion and have dinner. And E.T. did, and here is how it went:

"E.T., I would like for you to become the chancellor."

"Well, governor, I'm honored very much."

"I'm aware that that board is a constitutional board and they'll make the decision about who's chancellor, but I'm obviously going to be asked for my views," the governor said.

Wincing at the understatement and avoiding answering as he sometimes did, E.T. set about outlining for Governor Edmondson at some length the two big tasks he saw facing higher education in Oklahoma: the explosion in student population and the explosion in knowledge to be taught to them.

"To stand a chance to do a fair job for the people of Oklahoma I will require the full cooperation and teamwork of the governor, the legislature, the regents, and the college presidents under the leadership of the chancellor. I know there's a difference of views between the governor and legislative leaders and right now you and the legislative leadership don't get along. The legislative leaders are my friends and you're my friend, and I don't want to get caught in a trap."

Edmondson nodded his agreement and told E.T. that he understood and that E.T. had built a great institution at Eastern and had a beautiful campus and a good life.

"You wouldn't want to walk off into a dog's fight here without a reasonable chance of surviving. But, think about it."

Going out the door, E.T. put it to him straight:

"I'll tell you what, governor, we've got to get people together or I wouldn't bite into that trap at all."

In December, E.T. got a call from an old friend from the other side of the fence, House Speaker J.D. McCarty, with whom he had served in the legislature. By 1961, J.D. had come to be considered the second most powerful man in Oklahoma, and he was not considered second to the governor, but to Kerr, uncrowned king of the U.S. Senate. McCarty asked E.T. to come to Oklahoma City and have dinner with him.

And here is how that went:

"Why don't you take that job, E.T.? They tell me that you say no."

"J.D., now listen. The only way I can take that job would be for you and Howard Edmondson to get together, and right now you guys are just at one another's throats. You old boys in the two houses of the legislature connive and you whip our governor down, and he's going to appoint the regents that will hire the chancellor, and we'd have to all work together, and I don't see any chance of any teamwork there."

"Well," J.D. said, "it'll work out, E.T."

On December 17, Hinds called again:

"E.T.? Can you come to breakfast Saturday morning?"

They met in the Skirvin Tower Hotel, the most unlikely of Sunday breakfast companions: Governor J. Howard Edmondson, House Speaker J.D. McCarty, Everett Collins, president pro tem of the Senate, and E.T. Dunlap. The top brass of the Old Guard and the Crew Cuts, coming together in summit.

They said they were unanimous: "We want you to be our chancellor if the state regents will elect you, and we will work together on that. Whatever problems we have in other fields will not affect our views and attitudes toward support of higher education."

And they agreed to get E.T. some planning money, some money to hire staff and some money for research in getting ready to face those two huge challenges of the 1960s.

"Well," said E.T., "on that basis, if I'm offered the job, I'll take it."

Wharton Mathies was a country banker down in southeastern Oklahoma, and he was chairman of the state regents for higher education. He didn't like Howard Edmondson and had opposed him all the way. Edmondson realized where Mathies stood and largely returned the favor, and the fact that Mathies and the governor could feel about each other the way they did and Mathies remain in a powerful state position was a testimony to the distance Oklahoma lawmakers had put between higher education and politics. Mathies was a strong supporter of E.T. Dunlap for the chancellor's job.

"H.I.," said the governor, "get that old son of a bitch on the phone."

Later that day, Wharton called a special meeting of the State Regents for Higher Education. On the 19th of December, a Sunday, Elijah Thomas Dunlap turned 46 years old. And on the 21st of December, a Tuesday, he was elected chancellor of Oklahoma Higher education, effective July 1, 1961. The ranch kid from over the mountain who might never have gone to college if old J.O. Rich hadn't made that train trip to Oklahoma City back in 1934 became the number one man in Oklahoma higher education.

Hayden Donahue got scared. He had surgery for eye cataracts and was mostly blind for 37 days. Vision returned to his right eye, but he had no idea how long it would last. It came at a time when he was trying to set up a private practice in psychiatry, go out on his own with no guaranteed paycheck. Education expenses loomed for his three college-bound daughters.

But by 1961 when he became board eligible in psychiatry, some of his old friends back in Oklahoma were beginning to see what a blow it had been to the mental health system in Oklahoma when Donahue had left two years before. They began to call. Ask him to come back. His successor, they said, had gotten crossways with the legislature immediately and things had gone downhill since. Donahue refused to come back as director of mental health.

They offered him the superintendency of Central State Hospital in Norman and threw in a house for his use. They didn't have to ask twice. The Oklahoma kid from the other side of Peaceable Mountain was on his way back home. But, never, he told them, and don't even bother to ask, would he even consider again the heart- and body-breaking job of director of mental health for the State of Oklahoma.

29

'They Play as Tough and as Mean as That.'

"Kerr doesn't get his judge, and you don't get any tax legislation."

— ROBERT KENNEDY,
Attorney General
of the United States,
brother to the President

In 1961, through no intentional doing of his own, a 59-year-old Oklahoma City lawyer named Luther Lee Bohanon shut down the flow of legislation from the White House through the United States Congress, and nobody – not even Attorney General Robert Kennedy, brother to the President – could get it going again. It was the first time the name Luther Lee Bohanon had been tied to any happening of such national and international moment, but it was not to be the last. The story of how such a situation came to be starts – as do so many such stories – in a small south-eastern Oklahoma town and spans many years, eras, moods and administrations in Oklahoma and American history before reaching that day in 1961.

It was a crazy day in November of 1907. A six-year-old boy stood in his front yard and solemnly watched the throes as Oklahoma and Indian Territories birthed a state. Liquor in all forms and intensities was to be banned border to border at midnight. There were 556 saloons in Oklahoma Territory to be closed, and an uncounted number of bootleggers in Indian Territory, which supposedly had been dry forever. On that final day before statehood, men got drunk who had never been known to drink, and in the confusion some young boys got the first feel of fire in their bellies. Fights raged all day and into the night. But this six-year-old boy just stood solemnly in his front yard and watched. Mostly, he watched a horse.

It was in a bunch of horses set free from the livery stable by celebrating soon-to-be Oklahomans. It ran with its herd for a while, thundering down the street in panic, then – overcome by terror of the shouting and six-guns firing in the air – the horse veered into the boy's yard and ran headlong into a stump. Amid the revelry, the boy watched the horse die. At 11:50 p.m., the drunks were dragged into the streets, the lights were extinguished, and the doors were locked, and Oklahoma became a state. The ground on which the boy stood and watched the horse die became Haskell County.

Haskell County was where the luckier Choctaws settled who got to ride most of the way to their new country on steamboats instead of walking the Trail of Tears. It was named for Charles N. Haskell, Muskogee railroad promoter and land speculator who threw in with Bill Murray at the unsuccessful Indian Constitutional Convention and the successful Oklahoma Constitutional Convention and thus collected enough influence to became Oklahoma's first governor. Stigler, named for the man who developed the townsite, was made the county seat of Haskell County.

Haskell adjoins Pittsburg, McIntosh, and Latimer, becoming the northeast corner of a most fertile quadrant of counties in a manner of speaking. The boy was Luther Lee Bohanon. He would remember forever the day when residents of Indian and Oklahoma territories became full residents of the United States of America, with all the rights guaranteed to them by the United States Constitution. Most of all, he would remember that horse.

Next, he probably would remember best that day in April of 1961. U.S. Senator Robert S. Kerr – at the urging of his brother, Aubrey – called the 59-year-old Bohanon to his office and told him he was the senator's choice to be the next federal district judge from Oklahoma. Bohanon was not surprised.

On a sweltering Fourth of July in the year 1929 in the wild oil boom town of Seminole where he had moved to make himself some money, a young law school graduate named Luther Lee Bohanon ran into an old friend from their days at the University of Oklahoma. His name was Alfred Paul "Fish" Murrah. They sat under the shade tree and sipped Choctaw beer and talked about such people as their eloquent OU speech professor Joshua Bryan Lee who loved the spoken word so much he changed his middle name after hearing a soaring display of oratory from William Jennings Bryan. Luther Lee and Fish talked of such things from their past as men tend to do while sipping Choctaw beer and of their future which they agreed was uncertain. By day's end, they had become partners against that uncertainty.

The two young lawyers made some money trying compensation cases and such things in the rowdy oil town and then moved to Oklahoma City, where, by 1934, they decided to try their hand at politics. They got active in the campaigns of three men who were running for different district judgeships in Oklahoma and

Canadian counties. All three – Clarence Mills, George Giddings, Jr., and Ben Arnold won their races.

Then Joshua Bryan Lee called. He said he had decided to run for the U.S. House of Representatives from Oklahoma's Fifth District, and would they help. Together with another classmate, Royce Savage, they planned Lee's campaign. Got excited about it. Put up their own money and time, practicing law at night and at off hours. Joshua Lee won a seat in Congress, and his three former students earned themselves a pretty impressive political reputation and the nickname "The Rover Boys."

Two years later, Josh Lee ran for the U.S. Senate. The three Rover Boys again handled his campaign, and Lee finished first out of a field of eight in the Democratic primary, running well ahead of E.W. Marland, prominent oil executive, former New Deal member of Congress and sitting governor of the state of Oklahoma, and even farther ahead of the incumbent, Senator Thomas P. Gore, an institution in both Oklahoma politics and the Senate. And the political prowess of the Rover Boys went into Oklahoma history.

That same year, Congress created a fourth federal judgeship in Oklahoma to ease the growing burden on its courts. It was a roving position covering all three of the state's judicial districts. Fish Murrah wanted the judgeship, and Senator Josh Lee went to President Franklin D. Roosevelt and saw that he got it, no matter how fresh out of school he was. Fish became one of the youngest federal judges ever named. Nine years after he graduated from law school. In 1940, 14 years out of law school, Fish was named a United States Circuit Judge. Royce Savage, the other Rover Boy, was named federal judge for the Northern District of Oklahoma. That left one Rover boy not on the federal bench, but Luther Bohanon never seemed to mind.

He practiced law and lived his life and took care of his family, involving himself with some regularity in political campaigns. In

1938, Bohanon had branched out on his own and worked in the successful gubernatorial campaign of Leon "Red" Phillips. During that campaign he had worked closely with a politically ambitious young oilman-country lawyer named Robert S. Kerr who owned a little old hide house on the side, and his brother, Aubrey. And the friendship the three formed had lasted over the years.

In 1960, Oklahoma federal district judge William R. Wallace was killed in a car accident, and the vacancy was not filled before President Dwight D. Eisenhower was succeeded by President John F. Kennedy. That threw the selection of a federal judge to Robert S. Kerr who had, over the intervening years, transmuted himself from an ambitious young oilman-country lawyer who owned a little old hide house on the side to a former governor and reigning uncrowned king of the United States Senate. Numbered among a handful of the most powerful men in the United States. And he wanted the last of the Rover Boys to be a federal judge. And all that is why after all those years and eras and administrations of Oklahoma and America, Luther Lee Bohanon wasn't surprised when Robert S. Kerr called him to his office in Oklahoma City and told him that he and his brother Aubrey wanted him to be a federal judge. Nobody dreamed what would happen next.

Presidential candidates Nixon and Kennedy had agreed during the campaign that the winner would not appoint anyone whom the American Bar Association declined to endorse, continuing a policy established by President Eisenhower. The ABA, citing such things as Bohanon's age (59), and his heavy corporate experience rather than trial experience, and for other inexplicable and undefined reasons, declined to endorse him. Brash young Attorney General Robert Kennedy went with the bar association's position. He sent two young men to Senator Kerr asking that he withdraw the nomination of Bohanon and submit three other names.

Robert S. Kerr was the second-ranking Democrat on the Senate Finance Committee and the only man in Congress who could handle the committee's reactionary chairman, Harry Byrd of Virginia. With the departure of Lyndon B. Johnson from the Senate to become vice president, Kerr had become the most powerful and dominating man in the United States Senate. And he was accustomed to getting his way.

"I was here a long time before you came," he told the two young men sent by Robert Kennedy, "and I'm going to be here a long time after you go. My three names are, Bohanon, Bohanon, Bohanon."

Kerr was shepherding the major parts of Kennedy's 1961 legislative program – the highway bill, revision of aid to dependent children under Social Security, the temporary increase in the federal debt limit, water and air pollution legislation, expansion of unemployment compensation, funds for the administration's space program, and the administration's tax bills. He sent a message to the White House that if President Kennedy were unwilling to extend him the courtesy of nominating his choice for a federal judgeship, he might ought to look for somebody else to handle his legislation.

President Kennedy was preoccupied with the approaching Vienna summit conference and increasing Soviet pressure which resulted in the sealing of the borders of East Germany. Suddenly, his legislation stalled. In the Senate. President Kennedy sent a emissary to Kerr to see what was the problem.

"Tell him," Kerr said bluntly, "to get his dumb (bleeping) brother to quit opposing my friend."

State Senator Gene Stipe and other lawyers aware of Bohanon's qualifications for the job began circulating petitions statewide. Almost every lawyer in the state signed them. Still nothing happened. Kerr enlisted the aid of Oklahoma Governor J. Howard Edmondson, a close Kennedy confidant. Edmondson had been the only Oklahoma politician to support Kennedy for the Democratic nomination in 1960. Kerr had gone with his Senate associate, Lyndon Johnson.

Determined not to yield, Atty. Gen. Robert Kennedy sent his administrative assistant to Oklahoma to investigate Bohanon on his own. The investigator and the FBI both reported that the ABA's opposition was based on misinformation and recommended that the attorney general disregard the bar evaluation. Still nothing happened.

A man named Rex Hawks was one of Senator Kerr's key operatives. He was the man who attended meetings at which the senator did not want to be seen. Hawks had been a U.S. marshal during the administration of Harry Truman, and Kerr had nominated him to resume that job, but that appointment, too, had been stalled. Hawks went to see assistant attorney general Whizzer White to see what was going on. White assured Hawks that his own reappointment as a federal marshal was not the problem. He told Hawks that if Senator Kerr would simply make a recommendation other than Bohanon for the vacant federal judgeship, everybody could get back to their business. Hawks carried the message back to Kerr. The senator picked up the telephone. Called the President of the United States. Requested a personal, one-on-one conference at 5:30 that afternoon. Got it.

Nobody knows exactly what was said at that meeting, but the old political pro who had once owned a hide house and the young President who had grown up as a Boston millionaire, discovered they could speak the same language: You did not renege on a promise to a friend or to a brother. And Robert S. Kerr had given his word to both. There would be no compromise. The following day, August 17, 1961, the White House issued a special press release. It announced President Kennedy's intention to appoint Oklahoma City lawyer Luther Lee Bohanon as the next federal district judge from Oklahoma. On the day Bohanon's nomination reached the Capitol, the Senate passed the controversial Foreign Assistance Act of 1961. And the orderly flow of the nation's business resumed.

In autumn of that same year, as everyone still was cautiously congratulating themselves on how smoothly integration had gone in Oklahoma, a black Oklahoma City optometrist tried to enroll his son at the city's Northeast High School. When he was not permitted to, he filed a lawsuit. The lawsuit was handed to the newest federal judge on the bench.

Bohanon's grandfather, Lewis, had been killed in the Civil War, fighting for the Confederacy, but Luther had never had any particularly strong feelings about the problems of African-Americans or any other minority groups. He had learned what it was to be a member of a minority during his early days of schooling over in Blaine Bottom in the rough hill country of northern Haskell County.

Shortly after the fear-crazed horse ran into the tree stump and died in the Bohanon front yard in Stigler, federal restrictions on land ownership in the new Oklahoma ended. His daddy, William Bohanon, traded the family piano for a wagon and a team of mules, loaded up his family and furniture and moved onto a farm about seven miles northeast of Keota, south across the Arkansas River from Vian. Ten Bohanon children lived with their dad and stepmother in a two-room log cabin built on the side of a hill, just south of a large bluff that held its toes in Fish Creek. Young Luther Lee and his brothers and sisters were the only whites who went to school there. Every other face they could see in the schoolrooms was Choctaw Indian. And they had been received so graciously, it was hardly a handicap to be in the minority. So, Luther had never had cause to think about it a whole lot on a personal level until he was handed the lawsuit named Dowell vs the Oklahoma City School District. What he read in that suit appalled him.

As part of his homework, he picked up the landmark school integration case of Brown vs the Topeka Board of Education, and with his personal experience as a minority, his love of the law and the United States Constitution, it took his breath away.

Issued by the Supreme Court under Chief Justice Earl Warren, the opinion said bluntly that "segregation of white and Negro children in the public schools of a state solely on the basis of race ...

denies Negro children the equal protection of the laws guaranteed by the Fourteenth Amendment."

But, it did not say who would stop them from doing it.

The people filing the suit asked that it be given to a three-judge panel, and A.P. "Fish" Murrah, now chief judge of the Tenth Circuit Court of Appeals, convened a panel consisting of Murrah, Bohanon and U.S. District Court Judge Fred Daugherty. After a hearing, it was found that the case probably should be handled by a single judge and it was dropped back into the hands of the rookie judge. Bohanon confronted the crisis alone.

Two facts of state government became crystal clear in 1961. One was that the state Board of Affairs was unable to maintain the school for boys at Boley anywhere near an acceptable level. The Department of Human Services was asked to take over the school. Mr. Rader couldn't believe what he found. The boys wore coats in the dormitory in the winter because they had no heating. The roof didn't keep out the weather. The boys were getting only two meals a day because that's all the money the Board of Affairs had for them, and they complained they ate an awful lot of wild rabbit at those two meals. They had no supper and went to bed still wearing their coats. The school was a warehouse for miserable boys.

The second fact of government that became clear that year was that the Oklahoma Department of Human Services had become one of the best of its kind in the nation, gaining skill in gathering federal money and channeling it into the needs of the people of Oklahoma.

So, they put the two together, and asked the Department of Human Services to take over the boys school at Boley. Soon came Mr. Rader's people. They inventoried everything down to the staplers and the waste baskets. Mr. Rader was a businessman, and he wanted everything accounted for. And then the rebuilding could begin.

1963

On the night of June 12, President John F. Kennedy sent word ringing off the rafters that it was past time to end racial persecution of Negroes in the United States of America, and that he would see that it was done. A few moments later, civil rights worker Medgar Wiley Evers was shot down in the driveway of his home in Mississippi while his wife and two children waited for him inside. By August, 200,000 people were in the streets in Washington, D.C., demanding what Kennedy had promised. "I have a dream," Dr. Martin Luther King said, "that this nation will rise up and live out the true meaning of its creed, 'We hold these truths to be self-evident: that all men are created equal.'" J. Edgar Hoover, director of the Federal Bureau of Investigation, put King under surveillance, using wiretaps, electronic bugs and paid informants to gain information on his private life. Hoover circulated the worst of what he could gather in an effort to discredit the civil rights leader. King's popularity surged, anyway. In South Vietnam, President Ngo Dinh Diem was assassinated. The number of U.S. "advisers" ballooned to more than 15,000. Notice was served that they would fire back if fired upon. Aid to South Vietnam grew to more than $500 million.

And then, in November, the hardest thing of all: President John F. Kennedy was shot and killed as he rode in a motorcade through downtown Dallas, Tex. Vice Pres. Lyndon B. Johnson, Kerr's old Senate friend, was sworn in as President.

30

When Power Dies

New Year's Day, 1963. The Orange Bowl in Miami, Florida. On the field, the Alabama Crimson Tide with sophomore quarterback Joe Namath leading the offense was mauling Oklahoma's Sooners. And in the VIP section, Oklahoma's fire-haired young Governor J. Howard Edmondson was watching the game and talking politics with a personal friend of his, John F. Kennedy, President of the United States. There was a stir. The governor of Oklahoma rose suddenly and hurried with his entourage toward the exit. Something had happened. Something big enough to pull the young governor away from the President of the United States and an OU ballgame that hadn't been finished. Oklahoma finally lost the ballgame 17-0 after running back Jim Grisham fumbled the ball on the Alabama seven-yard line, nullifying a 56-yard Ron Fletcher-to-Allen Bumgardner pass, but that was nothing compared to the news that greeted departing Oklahomans when they turned on their car radios. Oklahoma's U.S. Senator Robert S. Kerr had just died. The big man who folded for five minutes out of the little plane and gave Joe Stipe his first campaign war chest. One of the last men to leave Kerr's bedside was Lloyd Rader.

When Robert S. Kerr had gone to Washington and Lloyd Rader had accepted the job as Oklahoma welfare director, the two had become a team. Mr. Rader's genius and Robert S. Kerr's power had grown in tandem. The two had shaped the beginnings of federal welfare. Kerr had provided the Senate staff and Rader had provided the knowledge. The original Kerr-Mills legislation later became Medicaid. They wrote the plans that later became Medicare. Saw to it that they were tailor made for Oklahomans.

"When I want to know something about welfare," Kerr told his colleagues, "I just look in my pocket and ask Lloyd Rader."

Kerr trusted what Mr. Rader told him. And Mr. Rader trusted what Bob Kerr told him, and they agreed that what was good for Oklahoma was good for the country. And that is why it was so hard for Lloyd Rader to leave the bedside of the dying king of the United States Senate.

The state went into mourning, and it wasn't just for the power lost. It was for a man born in a log cabin who became so arrogant he defied presidents and remained so humble he refused to stand in front of his humblest constituent in a political picnic food line. One of the most powerful men in the world who would take the time to attend the opening of a nursing home. Who would speak to a sixth-grade class with the same fervor he gave to an address before the graduates of Oklahoma University. A busy man who spent hours teaching his grandson the joys of fishing for black bass in Long Lake south of Poteau in the southeastern Oklahoma hills he loved. But there were those who were consumed by something other than grief at the news.

Kerr's death opened a political dream seat in the United States Senate. The governor of Oklahoma had the power to appoint somebody to serve in Kerr's place until the next general election in

1964. That incumbency would be a big leg up to being elected to serve out the last two years of Kerr's term, and then…?

Almost as fast as the news of Kerr's death arrived in Oklahoma, the scrambling began. Some Oklahoma political veterans thought Lieutenant Governor George Nigh had gone to the ballgame with Edmondson, leaving state government in the hands of Senate President Pro Tempore Everett Collins, second in line of succession to the governorship. One group launched an attempt to get Kirksey Nix appointed from the Court of Criminal Appeals to the United States Senate. Collins thought it was a great idea. They started the paperwork for the appointment, hoping to greet Edmondson with a completed coup when the governor returned. Others were scrambling for appointment of the governor's older brother, Congressman Ed Edmondson.

But J. Howard Edmondson, youngest governor in the history of Oklahoma, was not rushing to a memorial service for Senator Kerr. He had had a hurried and whispered conference with the President of the United States before their parting, and the two of them agreed on who should be sitting in that Senate seat when the campaigning began in 1964. Edmondson had left Lieutenant Governor George Nigh in charge in Oklahoma with full power of governor for so long as Edmondson was out of state. He had also left Nigh with explicit instructions to do absolutely nothing, no matter what happened, until he got back in the state. But, under these circumstances…

The governor hurried. Nursing his shocking choice for Oklahoma's new senator.

Nine days before the inauguration of his successor, Howard Edmondson resigned the governorship. Lieutenant Governor George Nigh became governor. Governor Nigh appointed Edmondson to the United States Senate.

In Washington, Senator Russell Long of Louisiana moved into the chairmanship of the United States Senate Finance Committee. He sent immediately for Mr. Rader.

For years, when Mr. Rader would go to Washington, he would take Gene with him. Mr. Rader already knew what he wanted to do when the two of them sat down to talk with United States senators, House members. When the congressmen proposed something that went contrary to what Mr. Rader thought ought to be done, Mr. Rader would turn and look at Gene:

"Our state legislature wouldn't do that, would they, Senator Stipe?"

"No, sir, they would not."

That, Gene came to feel, was the reason he was there. And so, when Mr. Rader called Gene to accompany him to Washington to see Senator Russell Long, Gene agreed. But it was a different kind of conference.

"Mr. Rader, I appreciate what you were doing for Senator Kerr," Senator Long said when they were seated in his office. "I want you to do the same thing for me."

And there was the faintest wisp of a smile.

"Except, now, you've got to look after Louisiana like you've been looking after Oklahoma."

And Mr. Rader took Senator Long's committee staff and began recalculating the formulas. And when Medicare and Medicaid finally grew to fruition in the middle 1960s, everybody wondered why Oklahoma seemed, somehow, always to fare better in the formulas than any other state in the union. Except, of course, Louisiana.

Governor George Nigh's nine-day reign was a hectic one for state Senator Stipe. Arrangements crafted carefully around the power of Senator Kerr began to come unraveled.

Back in 1962, Gene and some southeastern Oklahoma legislators had got together with Leland Gourley, Henryetta publisher and a top aide of Edmondson's, and were trying to get Arrowhead and Fountainhead state lodges built on the new Lake Eufaula which was nearing completion. The lodges would, they contended, bring an influx of jobs and money into the financially depressed southeast during construction and a tourist boom after their completion. Under pressure from the state senators, the governor's office and Senator Kerr, the Oklahoma Planning and Resources Board had applied for a grant from the federal Economic Development Administration to build the lodges, over the protests of some other state senators – including Gene's sometimes roommate Ray Fine of Gore – who already had their lodges and could see no reason to build lodges nicer than their own to bleed away their customers. Gene had gone with a delegation to Washington to meet with representatives of Economic Development who would make a decision on whether the federal government would lend the state money for construction of the lodges. Kerr, by then chairman of the Senate Finance Committee, Carl Albert, by then Democratic whip of the House, and Congressman Ed Edmondson were among those who had gathered to support them. The director of the agency dug in his heels.

"This funding of state lodges is not one of our missions," he told the legislators. Senator Kerr stood up.

"I want you to recess this meeting until in the morning," Senator Kerr told him, "and I want you to take your counsel and take the time between now and then to review a little more carefully the statute that states your mission. I'm absolutely certain you will find this project is precisely the kind of thing we contemplated when we passed that legislation."

And he sat down. And the meeting adjourned.

When the delegation showed up the next morning, sure enough, Senator Kerr was right. The federal bureaucrats had discovered that building two lodges on Lake Eufaula was just exactly the mission of that agency, and so Oklahoma got the green light to build the lodges. And that was the kind of influence Senator Bob Kerr had exerted for Oklahoma in Washington. And it was quickly missed.

The contracts were not yet signed when the senator died. Governor Edmondson left for Washington as an interim freshman senator, and Oklahoma had a new and temporary governor. The Oklahoma Planning and Resources Board wouldn't sign the contract to operate the lodges. Nigh called Washington to see if the loan could be delayed. He was told that if action wasn't taken, the state might lose the loan. Nigh didn't want his nine-day reign as governor to go down in history as the one that lost a $9 million economic development loan for southeastern Oklahoma. Gene rushed over to the capitol when he got the news. Nigh was wringing his hands.

"What do we do, Gene?"

"Fire the board and appoint another one, George."

As the night waned, the brand-new governor – who also happened to be from McAlester – methodically fired each rebellious member of the Planning and Resources Board and appointed new ones, calling around to get the new members to accept their positions and get on the road to Oklahoma City to sign the contract for construction of the lodges.

When the first rays of the morning sun found their way into the Blue Room of the State Capitol, the new board members were putting their names on their first official contract. It was for construction of Arrowhead and Fountainhead State Lodges on the state's new Lake Eufaula. It was the only night, Gene would chuckle, that he ever spent in the governor's mansion.

On Jan. 14, 1963, a Billings wheat farmer named Henry Bellmon was sworn in as the first Republican governor in the history of the State of Oklahoma, ending 56 years of Democrat domination. A dozen Democrats had gone haggling after the nomination, ranging from former Governor Raymond Gary to Oklahoma's premier rebel attorney, Tomy Dee Frasier of Tulsa. Others included Lieutenant Governor George Nigh, and ultra-liberal state senator Fred Harris. Midwest City millionaire Bill

Atkinson won the nomination. Bellmon defeated him in an election that turned on whether there would be any additional taxes levied against Oklahomans for the next four years. It wasn't even close.

Settled into his office, Bellmon set out to show the people of Oklahoma how their first Republican governor could run the state efficiently on the money it had in hand. Then, his wife made one of those nice gubernatorial-spouse visitations. She dropped by one of the state-sponsored homes for the mentally retarded. She was horrified beyond politics. The children, she scolded to her husband, were tied out to the trees in the yard to keep them out of trouble while their supervisors were gone. She demanded that her husband do something about the state's facilities for the mentally retarded. A general overhaul, she insisted, was in order. New taxes or no new taxes. When Bellmon put pencil to paper, he, too, was horrified. He found a $22 million hole in the budget.

And the state's latest attempt to help the mentally retarded was bankrupt. It was Hissom Memorial Center still under construction at Sand Springs. There wasn't enough money in the budget even to finish it. And so, disaster loomed for the first Republican administration in the history of the State of Oklahoma. Henry Bellmon went over for a visit with Lloyd Rader.

When they told him the governor was there, Mr. Rader remembered with a smile the telephone call he had gotten from his worried brother, Dean, when Bellmon began to take on all the aspects of a winner.

"This Bellmon fellow says he intends to throw all of the old guard out, Lloyd," Dean said. "What are you going to do if he wins?"

"I'm not part of the old guard, Dean. I was here before the old guard got here."

31

'You Fellas Been Listening to Roscoe Dunjee'

Judge Luther Bohanon struck down a section of the Oklahoma Constitution that had been there since old Bill Murray held it between his knees to keep anybody from tampering with it. It said, "Separate schools for white and colored children with like accommodation shall be provided by the Legislature and impartially maintained. The term 'colored children,' shall be construed to mean children of African descent. The term white children shall include all other children."

Bohanon also rooted out the Oklahoma statutes that had been passed by the legislature as authorized by that section of the constitution.

In 1954, the United States Supreme Court had said clearly that racially segregated schools were not equal, could never be made equal, and that attempts to maintain separate education facilities inevitably deprived black children of equal opportunities. Southerners had ignored it, and the Supreme Court hadn't given anybody the job of enforcing it. So, by the time the Oklahoma City school case was handed to Luther Bohanon, only one percent of Negro students in the South attended desegregated schools. Alabama Governor George Wallace summed up Southern feelings:

"I draw the line in the dust," he said, "and toss the gauntlet before the feet of tyranny and I say segregation now, segregation tomorrow, segregation forever."

Judge Luther Bohanon had never been one to stop at lines in the dust. The Oklahoma City School Board, he said, was enforcing an illegal, discriminatory educational system, and had spun a "sad tale of deception," to hide what it was doing.

"One of the basic foundations of America's strength, and one of the keys to its greatness, is the right to have equal public schools for all our children. If any white child were denied such right all would be indignant; why not let it be so with our Negro children."

Bohanon was clear on who would enforce it. He would. He gave the Oklahoma City School Board ninety days to develop a comprehensive integration plan. And, he went one step further.

When integration had begun in rural school districts in 1955-56, black students simply had been sent to white schools. Black schools – and their faculties – had been abandoned. It had left more than 300 black teachers and administrators without jobs. Most were forced to move out of state to find work. Bohanon ordered integration of faculty and staff as well as students.

Back when Bill Murray and those who thought as he did controlled government in Oklahoma, Murray had dismissed black protest offhandedly: "You fellas," he would say, "have been listening to Roscoe Dunjee, and he's a hundred years ahead of his time."

Turned out, Alfalfa Bill was almost a half-century off. Judge Bohanon struck down the last written excuse for a segregated school system in Oklahoma fifty-six years after that scared-crazy old horse ran into the tree in his front yard and died on the day Oklahoma became a state.

Hissom Memorial Center joined the flow of state institutions under the wing of the Department of Public Welfare. And thus Governor Henry Bellmon, one of the most trusted men in Oklahoma, lived up to his campaign promise to keep Oklahoma strong with no new taxes. Lloyd Rader, he would say privately, saved his administration. And Lloyd Rader, the old inveterate Democrat who had driven Alfalfa Bill Murray around Western Oklahoma, became a close friend of the wheat farmer from Billings who had become Oklahoma's first Republican governor. When Hissom was dedicated in 1964, Governor Bellmon proudly announced it "places Oklahoma in the forefront of such activity in the United States," the ultimate treatment facility for people with developmental disabilities. And Mrs. Bellmon could visit the state's facility for the mentally retarded without wanting so much to cry.

In that year, the Legislature also gave Mr. Rader the Enid State School and the Pauls Valley State School. Governor Bellmon signed an executive order designating the welfare department as the sole state agency to receive grants of federal funds for combating or preventing mental retardation. And Oklahoma's entire system of care for the mentally disabled had passed, unasked, into the hands of Binger Trading Company co-owner Lloyd Rader.

Mr. Rader paid his first visit to the Enid State School during lunch hour, and what he saw appalled him. After the children had been fed lunch, they were given individual syrup-type buckets with a snap-down lid. Workers put the leftover pudding in the bottom of the bucket, and then they put the bread on top of that, and then they put in whatever else was left of the noontime meal. It set there until suppertime and that is what the residents of Enid State School ate for supper. It was the last such supper ever served to the children at Enid State School.

32

Go-Go Girls in Gingham

Since Joe Stipe had left little-boy games back on Peaceable Mountain to listen to the old men swap stories, a love for people stories had grown.

State Senator Gene Stipe had begun, by the late 50s and early 60s to emerge as one of Oklahoma's leading folk storytellers. He collected stories as some people collect autographed baseballs or pictures of celebrities. Let's listen to one:

> I had some folks hire me. They'd been picked up for passing counterfeit twenty-dollar bills. Couple of gals. They were go-go dancers from Oklahoma City. And, there wasn't that much defense, they were passing counterfeit twenties. They had a couple of hundred of them. They'd passed 'em to everybody in town.
>
> There was an old federal judge over at Fort Smith, Judge Miller. He had a very colorful history. He had been elected to the United States Senate as an independent candidate

during the Roosevelt days, and Roosevelt wanted real bad to have a Democrat in the Senate from Arkansas. So the old judge – all he had ever wanted to do was be a federal judge. The only reason he ran for U.S. Senate, he wanted to be a federal judge. So they made a trade. Roosevelt appointed him as federal judge and the governor appointed whoever Roosevelt wanted as U.S. Senator. It's a colorful bit of Arkansas history.

I always liked Judge Miller because he was a great judge and kind of a country old guy, and he kind of took a fancy to me, and he was always nice to me. I was representing the mine workers union and we had a old lawyer over there named Love Grant. He was kind of my boss. He was one of the organizers of the mine workers. He introduced me to Judge Miller.

Judge Miller had grown up out in the country in Arkansas. His family was farmers, family of sharecroppers. He'd talk on and on about picking cotton. Now, you can't influence the sentencing much in federal cases, because the probation officers do the pre-sentencing investigations, and they do their reports, and that is what the judge bases the sentence on. They don't ask the defense lawyer for any comments so you don't have any chance to input to them. But they do interview the defendants.

So, knowing Judge Miller's background, I kind of coached those gals a little bit about what to tell the probation officers. They had a pretty good story about growing up on a country farm and chopping cotton and picking cotton. I had those go-go girls dressed up in pretty gingham dresses, you know, and the judge, he was fixing to really lay the wood to them, and I could see his mind, almost, working while he was reading that report. But, when he got to where they picked and chopped cotton on a sharecropper farm, he looked up from that report, and there they were in their gingham dresses, and damned if he didn't give them probation.

The Secret Service was beside themselves, because they had already told me there had never been a counterfeiter get probation. Never had been. They were really exercised about it. They tried to take an appeal of the judge's decision. Couldn't do it. They never did know how I got that done. But, old Judge Miller was a great American. A great old Arkansas country American. And I knew that.

Those were the only clients I ever had that I wouldn't take cash. I made 'em go get me a check.

George Miller, an Ada television executive, began his first term in the Oklahoma State Senate in 1965. Being young and enthusiastic, he set out across his new district to see what was going on. There had been a big scandal the year before about the Oklahoma Department of Education putting carpets in the Oklahoma School for the Deaf at Sulphur. Many considered that an unacceptable extravagance. Miller had never been to the school, so he went there first to see the famous carpets. He was appalled, but not at the carpet. There was not a roof that didn't leak. There were holes in the wall that you could throw a cat through. The place stunk.

"There is no money to fix it," the administrator said. "The carpet was for the acoustical effect on the deaf children."

Oklahoma did not mainstream children with disabilities. If you had a deaf child and you could not afford to send them to a private school, they went to the school for the deaf when they were about four years old. George was the father of young children. It tore him up. Little, disabled children subjected to this.

Senator John Luton of Muskogee was elected to the state Senate for the first time that year, too. He acquired as part of his district the School for the Blind. And he visited it. He, too, was appalled. Blind children had to feel their way up and down stairs. There were no sheltered passageways connecting buildings for when the snow and sleet blew. Many times the heat wouldn't work in the classrooms, and they didn't even have heat in the dormitory

The two freshmen senators got together. What could two first-termers do in a Legislature dominated by seniority?

They looked at each other and came to the same conclusion.

"Lloyd Rader."

They introduced a bill to transfer the Oklahoma School for the Deaf and the Oklahoma School for the Blind to the Department of Welfare.

Within a year, the schools were transformed. Not only was the heat made to come on and the buildings renovated and made modern, but certified teachers had taken over instruction and the two young senators had schools to brag to their homefolks about. Lloyd Rader let the young freshmen do all of the announcing of the improvements.

Senator George Miller decided that he would stay close to Mr. Lloyd Rader if he could.

33

Mr. Bailey, Brown Eggs and Turnpike Passes

It always seemed to Gene like an eternal trip to anywhere if you started in McAlester. Almost as far to Henryetta, it seemed, on the crooked little backroads as it would be to Tulsa on a straight line. Along in the '60s, he decided his hometown needed a turnpike. One that would hook in with Interstate 40 at Henryetta and lead to all points beyond. Link McAlester with the world. The Turner Turnpike was by now a proven old-timer; The Will Rogers Turnpike that connected to the Turner at Tulsa and took it to the Missouri line near Joplin had opened in 1957; another turnpike from Oklahoma City through Lawton to the Texas state line had opened in 1964, and it had been named for H.E. Bailey himself. It was time McAlester had a turnpike, and H.E. Bailey still was the man you went to if you wanted to talk about highways in Oklahoma. Gene had learned in his first year in the Legislature that you didn't just stomp into H.E. Bailey's office and try to tell him what he was going to do. You had to do it right. So, Gene thought of George Hall.

George Hall was a halfblood Indian who looked like a full-blood. George was a great character. Loved turnpikes. He had acquired for the state the right of way for the Will Rogers Turnpike, and he was always interested in seeing more roads built because he would usually end up getting some work out of it. George Hall knew how to get along with Mr. Bailey. Knew some things on him that not a lot of folks knew. Gene got to visiting with George about how much McAlester needed a turnpike to get out of there to anywhere, and, of course, George agreed with him. So, George told Gene what he knew on Harry Bailey.

Mr. Bailey had a passion for eggs.

Old-time farm eggs where the chickens had scratched in the barnyard and out in the fields and produced those thick, deep yellow yolks to which the yolks of mass-produced eggs bore slight resemblance. But, they couldn't be just any range-run eggs, they had to be brown. Laid, usually, by the Rhode Island Red hen of the old-time farmstead.

So, Gene and George Hall started dropping by and visiting with Mr. Bailey. Every month or so, just visit with him. George would always have some brown eggs located with all the prerequisites, and the two would go by to visit with Mr. Bailey and take him several dozen brown eggs and talk turnpikes. Hell of a deal. Mr. Bailey was tickled to death to get brown eggs, and pretty soon, he was just tickled to death to see Gene and George Hall walk into his office because he knew he was going to get several dozen brown eggs. Building a turnpike takes a lot of planning and advance work, so to speak, and somebody's got to put in the time and the thought to do it. Before long, Gene and Mr. Bailey and George Hall had put together a workable idea to build a turnpike from McAlester to Interstate 40 at Henryetta, and thus to the world.

On January 1, 1966, the McAlester-to-Henryetta section of the Indian Nation Turnpike, opened, and Gene had a direct route out of town to the world. But, that was far from being the only thing of political note to occur in McAlester that year.

A future attorney general of the State of Oklahoma came to town and met old Carl Bernethie, the mule man, Pres Lester's hatchet man in that famous political race back in 1930 that political oldtimers in Pittsburg County still chuckled over in 1966. And that meeting made quite a splash of its own, at least to those who were in on it. Here is how it happened.

Oklahoma had elected its first Republican governor in history four years before, and the sky hadn't fallen. Another was running for governor in 1966 with a good chance of winning. So G.T. Blankenship, a mild, gentlemanly Republican, filed as a candidate to be his attorney general. Knowing Gene as friendly and helpful when they had served together in the House of Representatives – even if Gene was a Democrat – G.T. drove down to McAlester before the primary election and asked Gene for some tips on where and how he should campaign Pittsburg County, deep as it was in the heart of Democratic Little Dixie.

"I don't know any Republicans down here, G.T.," Gene told him. "Best place, I guess, would be up at the courthouse. They claim Republicans pay their taxes just like Democrats. Just kind of see who comes in, shake hands with 'em, campaign 'em."

Gene happened by the courthouse later, and G.T. was standing out there doing as he had been advised, shaking hands and grinning. And there on the street was old Carl Bernethie. He was an even more colorful figure by then, with 30 more years of living on him. He was a constable, barely five-feet-two, wearing a bright red bandanna, a big black hat, and a gun so long it almost dragged the ground. Gene was struck by how much he looked like the cartoon strip character, Tumbleweeds. G.T. was grinning and shaking hands and Gene could see he was working his way toward Carl Bernethie. Gene eased up beside G.T. and stood there, watching him politick.

"Gene?" G.T. said in a quiet aside, "who's that colorful-looking gentleman over there?"

"That's Officer Bernethie, G.T. Very influential person here. Don't know if he's Democrat or Republican. Go get acquainted with him, maybe he'll help you."

Chuckling, Gene started to walk away, then paused. Went back.

"If you want to make him feel good..." Gene said it in a low, conspiratorial voice. "Tell him you heard all about his mules."

G.T. was nodding enthusiastic understanding when Gene walked away. Gene went into the courthouse and told the county clerk what he had done, then walked across the street and into a store so he could watch. G.T. walked up to old Carl grinning, bent forward in that gentlemanly way to shake his hand, leaned in close to speak something confidentially. And all of a sudden Gene saw Constable Carl Bernethie stiffen and it looked almost as if he were grabbing at his gun. Gene could see the spit flying.

The county clerk was laughing so hard he could barely answer the telephone.

"Good thing old Carl couldn't draw his gun," he told Gene, "he'd a shot him."

Gene hunted up a shaken G.T. Blankenship.

"Did you meet Mr. Bernethie?"

G.T.'s eyes widened.

"Why, yes I did. He's rather a volatile individual, isn't he?"

Gene confided to friends later that he would have felt real bad if Carl had shot G.T.

"Even if he was a Republican."

Gentlemanly G.T. Blankenship never knew what he had said that had offended the little man so mightily.

With all the land acquisition work he had done and all the brown eggs he had hauled to Mr. Bailey, George Hall got to thinking that if anybody in the state of Oklahoma had a free pass on the turnpike, he ought to have a free pass on the turnpike. And the one thing Mr. Bailey wouldn't do was give anybody a free pass on the turnpike. More and more often, the time Gene spent with George Hall was listening to him complain about cranky Mr. Bailey who was too stingy to give him a pass to the turnpike.

Almost patiently, Harry Bailey would explain it to George.

"Nobody gets a pass on the turnpike, George."

But George Hall never got to where he could accept it. It ceased to be a matter of privilege or money and became a matter of honor. As time went on, George began to suspicion that Harry Bailey was handing out turnpike passes to people he liked better than he liked George Hall, who was the only one who had ever brought him brown eggs, along with Senator Stipe. George just never did think that was right, and he would tell you so at the drop of a hat.

One day George and Gene were scheduled to go up to see Mr. Bailey, but Gene had to be in court in Tulsa first. Arriving at the Tulsa turnpike gate, Gene motioned the gatekeeper in close, talked earnestly with him for a moment, handed him a double fare, and went on. Gene did his business in Tulsa and picked up George, and George was sitting there in the passenger seat as Gene's Cadillac approached the toll booth for the second time that day and slowed to pay.

The gatekeeper waved him off with a wide smile and a grand sweep of his arm:

"Go on through, Gene, your pass is good!"

George sat in silence while the miles slid past. Gene could see him puffing up. Tighter and tighter. Like an over-filled balloon. About eleven miles out of Henryetta, George exploded. Waving his arms and cussing and yelling.

"Goddamned old lying son of a bitch!"

"What's the matter, George?"

"That old son of a bitch has been lying to me all these years!"

"Why do you say that?"

"You know you've got a pass and that old son of a bitch won't give me one."

Then, George Hall formulated another plan based on a billowing resentment built up over several years and many brown eggs: He was going to hit Mr. Bailey right in the mouth.

In the parking lot outside the Turnpike Authority, Gene finally had to tell him about the joke. And sit with him until he cooled down enough to say the words H.E. Bailey without spewing anger onto the windshield.

34

Wanted: Private Pilot (Some Cowardice Preferred)

It was two o'clock in the morning, and McAlester airport was black. Especially from Gene's perch in the pilot seat of the little tricycle-gear airplane. There were no runway lights. Only the flashing beacon atop the Masonic Temple, the distant glow of the prison. Then, Gene remembered something that should have occurred to him before he checked out of his motel in Lubbock, Tex., so late at night and decided to fly back home unannounced. McAlester had started turning off the runway lights late at night to save power costs.

Gene had been in Lubbock, Texas, buying a ranch. Flew out by himself, took two or three days to get the deal closed, got it closed the evening before and decided against spending another night in the motel although he already had his room rent paid. He just headed out to the Lubbock airport, got in his plane and started home. It had been a quiet, pleasant trip, but now he didn't know where the runway was. No way in the dark to tell the runway from any other flat spots in the rolling fields that surrounded McAlester.

There was supposed to be an operator at the airport all night. Kind of like a service station. Call him, he would turn the lights on. Gene got on the radio. Nobody answered.

Gene loved the little airplane. Bought it in partnership back in 1956 with Charlie Anderson. Charlie was a big contractor. Good guy. Built Pine Creek Reservoir. It was the first tricycle-gear airplane to be built. Probably the most efficient, least troublesome plane ever put together. But even it needed a lighted place to land. Gene called the airport again. Nobody answered.

It was pleasant, up there alone. Peaceable Mountain off to the south under its blanket of darkness, the prison a bright-speckled glow to the northwest. But the runway? Gene circled for a half-hour. Flew lower. There was the runway, looked like. He hung up the mike and made a low pass. He could definitely see it now, looming a slight pale out of the darkness. He lined up for his approach. He'd land in the dark and then hunt up the old boy who was supposed to be there and give him what for. He knew he could see the runway. At least he was pretty sure he could. He braced himself, sucked his lower lip into his mouth in intense concentration.

"We can't find him."
They woke Agnes from a sound sleep.
"But the plane's tore up."
Told her about it over the telephone.
"Blood all over."

Gene admitted later to friends that he had made two miscalculations, one minor and one severe.

His minor miscalculation was made in the dark. He had landed on the nose wheel. Felt the shock wave shudder through the little plane as it tipped and slammed forward. Felt his teeth cut through the lip he had sucked into his mouth. By the time everything had stopped crashing and the little plane had come to a halt, the blood was flowing from his lip and down over his clothes so that he forgot about hunting up the guy who wouldn't turn on the lights. He found his car and drove himself to the hospital to be sewn up. His severe miscalculation was that he did not call Agnes. He made that assessment shortly after he opened the door to his home and interrupted her in her early morning death watch for her lost husband.

The compromise was that he would get himself a pilot. A coward. One who would not dream of trying to land at two o'clock in the morning on a dark runway. Even in that great little tricycle-gear airplane.

❖

Wade finally had himself a good political job. He was an assistant sergeant at arms in the Oklahoma State Senate in addition to being an every-other-Sunday preacher at two little churches which meant he could preach every Sunday. He loved it. And he hadn't had to climb into the back of that old pickup truck or do any of the things he had done for Bob Kerr or Bill Coe or all those other people he had so hoped would help him. What he had done was to get better acquainted with the young state senator from Peaceable Mountain whom he had campaigned against for Kirksey Nix back in 1954.

Wade had been elected state president of the NAACP, a direct, in-line successor to Roscoe Dunjee. As such, he had to visit local chapters of the NAACP. Gene had been elected state commander of the American Legion, and included in his duties were visits to local legion posts to install officers and such. The two of them discovered their meetings could be planned so as to coincide in time and location. So, they drove together. Blackwell one night, next night in Lawton, Ardmore, Poteau, or Jay or wherever. Each collected mileage from his organization, and they pooled expenses and made it on a slim budget. They traveled so much together one of Wade's opponents as candidate for NAACP president once accused him of having a white chauffeur.

Judge Bohanon still hadn't said anything about integration of cafes and such, so Wade and Gene sort of waged their own civil rights movement. With wit. The stories that built up around their travels had – as Gene was wont to say – considerable truth in them. Here's one:

One night, they stopped off at Shawnee at a truck stop to have breakfast. The waitress kept circling around and signaling to Gene. He had no idea what she was trying to say. Finally, she just said it: "I'm sorry sir, we don't serve Negroes here."

Wade grinned.

"I don't mind that," he said, "I don't eat them anyway. I just want some ham and eggs like the senator's having."

They laughed together hungry all the way to the car.

Henry Bellmon, Oklahoma's first Republican governor was elected to the U.S. Senate that year.

He never really quit being a farmer. The field sown to politics instead of wheat. Always got up at daylight. Bellmon called Gene a lot and that was okay when both of them were in the same time zone. But, when Bellmon went to Washington, he would call at 6 o'clock in the morning there, and it would be five o'clock in the morning in Oklahoma. That was pretty darned early, even for an old Peaceable Mountain boy.

part four

He was the perfect witness. A kindly old country doctor, brushing back the white hair and looking out at the court with eyes gentled even further by popbottle glasses. Telling them eye to eye the atrocities he had seen done to the minds of men who had been forced to deal with death too long. With a wistful kind of sadness. Making them feel it inside their own heads.

1970 *Seemed like the disillusionment started back in the sixties and just kept growing. In March of '68, FBI Director J. Edgar Hoover wrote a memo for his people that said the Rev. Martin Luther King, Jr., had the potential to rise as a new messiah and mold his black followers into a secret terrorist organization like the Mau Mau that brutalized whites in Kenya in the early 1950s. On April 4, King was shot dead as he stepped out on the balcony of his Memphis motel room. Still only 39, King was killed with one shot fired from a 30.06 Remington rifle. Race riots erupted at Baltimore, Boston, Chicago, Detroit, Kansas City, Newark, Washington, D.C. In Chicago, Mayor Daley gave police shoot-to-kill orders. Before it was all over, 46 Americans had been killed across the nation. By Americans.*

Bobby Kennedy, brother to the assassinated John F. Kennedy, was killed before he could even complete his bid for the presidency, and Jackie Kennedy, America's First Lady of Camelot, widow of JFK, married aging Greek millionaire Aristotle Onassis. But the greatest disillusionment of all just kept building and building over the tiny Asian nation of Vietnam, and what was happening to American boys who were sent there to protect their moms and dads and sisters and brothers back home.

35

Vietnamization

Near sundown, I ate my Last Supper, put on my gear, and we moved out into the bush with Schwartz leading the way. We took it a little more carefully than usual. I was carrying the M-79 grenade launcher, and I had a buckshot round in it and four extras on my belt. For an hour nothing happened. Then, Schwartz stopped in the thick darkness and held up his hand. He came back a few steps and motioned for me to join him, finger to his lips. Male voices! At this time of night they had to be Cong. I signaled for the other three to move up. The five of us rounded the bend. Three huts, barely visible in the night. Again we heard the men's voices. We moved in closer. Suddenly there was silence.

In June of 1969, in response to growing pressure as more and more American soldiers died, President Richard M. Nixon had announced the beginning of U.S. troop withdrawal and a new Vietnamization policy to extricate America from that strange war. But by March of 1970 in the steamy killing jungles of central South Vietnam, nobody was noticing much of anything different, except that there were fewer men to fight the same dirty war.

Approaching the first hut, I motioned Schwartz to step inside while the rest of us waited, weapons trained on the doorway. Schwartz came out hauling two women and two older boys. We went into the other two huts and brought out more women and children. We stood them in the yard in front of the huts to question them about the men's voices we had heard. They were no more than black lumps until the flashlight swept across their faces. Then we could see the widened eyes and grimly drawn mouths. We needed to move out quickly.

For days the killing of the young Marine's friends had been going on. Six in an ambush. Then First-Sergeant Lyons. The toll was up to 15 or 20. Booby traps. Three more dead. Friends and acquaintances dead so quick you couldn't keep track. United States Marines being torn to pieces by men, women and children who smiled and waved from their farm fields in daytime, then struck quick as snakes in the thick dark of a jungle night and were gone before you knew death had been there. It centered in Sector 4, Queson Valley, central Vietnam. The village called Son Trang 4. These three huts.

A bullet whizzed by my head, I saw a burst of fire, and heard a loud thwack. One woman reached under her pajamas; another made a sudden dash. There was another burst of fire.

"Shoot!" I shouted. "Kill them all."

I fired the M-79 and the grenade exploded in orange flame. The others blasted away, and for ten seconds the night was lit with tracers. I could see flashes of fire behind the scattering Vietnamese as they stumbled and fell to the ground.

Then the firing was over. Silence surrounded us.

"Jesus!" I heard someone whisper.

"Let's get out of here!" I shouted.

"God, we killed a bunch of civilians. Women and children."

We ran back down the path, firing bursts into the darkness. I held up my hand. We stopped, trying not to breathe. We heard them in the bush. They were coming.

It took all Gene had to meet the eyes of the gangly half-Creek-Indian kid in sweaty Marine camouflage utilities. He was from Calvin, for heaven's sake, in Oklahoma. Hughes County. Had grown up running the red sandy banks of the Canadian River in the peanut country in the western edge of Gene's senatorial district. Not much older than Gene had been when he volunteered for the Navy and got sent off to flight school instead of to war.

"You've got to accept the idea," Gene said, "that you may hear yourself pronounced guilty and sentenced to life in prison."

The boy's eyes flinched. Turned queasy.

"You're telling me we are going to lose this trial?"

"That's about it."

"No chance?"

"Slim to none."

The boy stiffened and discipline took over. Gene wanted to cuss or kick a rock. The kid wasn't in Calvin, Oklahoma, now. He was standing on the side of a hill that sloped down to the South China Sea in the still-flaming core of a war for which America had shaped him and then decided it didn't want the war any more.

The crash educational program that had started in the United States when Russia orbited its dog around the earth had finally paid off. Snow-white-clad Neil Armstrong had become the first human to set foot on the moon – in brilliant television color in the living rooms of millions of Americans. And that is what America wanted to see now. For every two American boys threading the black jungle backpaths trying to kill the deadly Viet Cong in their names, there was one young American on the streets of Washington, D.C., calling it murder. Police had had to surround the White House with D.C. Transit buses parked bumper to bumper to keep them back from the White House where President Nixon sat watching a football game on television. Unable to sleep, sometimes, Nixon would arise before dawn, and go onto the street to try to talk with the young demonstrators. All the frustration over Vietnam that was tearing the nation apart was circling hungrily for a place to settle. And Gene did not want it to be on the head of this good-natured half-Indian kid from the peanut country on the western edge of his senatorial district.

"Are you a United States senator?"

Gene had grinned at the Marine colonel back in the states.

"What do you think I am, a Mexican?"

And the colonel had grinned apologetically and booked him onto the charter military flight from Hamilton Air Force Base in California as United States Senator Gene Stipe. And everywhere the plane landed, they had taken him off first, and a colonel was waiting to see him to be sure his trip was going okay. In Saigon, he was billeted in the VIP headquarters, a block from the castle where the Vietnam leaders lived. That was gratifying until he learned that the Viet Cong fired rockets at the castle every night and they never hit the castle. VIP headquarters was in the near-miss zone.

The surgeon general of the Navy was there, three stars, maybe four. They had dinner together, and after dinner the admiral decided to go for a walk. Gene declined, remembering his escorting colonel's advice about walking in that city at night. The admiral's saunter about Saigon ended abruptly and he returned to the billet without the trousers to his impressive admiral's uniform. A mob of street urchins had set upon him not far from the hotel and had not taken time, there on the street, to search through the trousers for wallet and other valuables. They had taken the trousers. Most embarrassing of all, the admiral confessed, was that the oldest urchin was only about ten years old.

The military courtesies extended to a United States senator followed Gene all the way to Da Nang. They even saw to it that he had good linens for his bunk. But that was before they knew why he was there.

Late in 1969, a story had come to light that sickened the combined conscience of the war-weary American people. They learned that on March 16, 1968, U.S. soldiers of C Company, First Battalion, Twentieth Infantry, Eleventh Brigade, Americal Division, led by Lieutenant William L. Calley, had invaded the South Vietnamese hamlet of My Lai, an alleged Viet Cong stronghold, and shot to death 347 unarmed civilians, including women and children. A secret Army investigation said it was more than murder. There was rape, they said, sodomy and maiming. The Army had tried to hide it and, when it became known, to minimize it. Army heads still were rolling. The commander of the troops was convicted of murder. Even the superintendent of the U.S. Military Academy at West Point – who had commanded the Americal Division – had resigned. Anti-war demonstrators jammed the streets of America.

And at the height of all this international emotion, this 19-year-old kid from the peanut country of Oklahoma had followed orders to lead his patrol into a Viet Cong village called Son Trang 4 in the Queson Valley. When daylight came, a reconnaissance patrol led by an officer new to combat found sixteen people there on the ground in front of the three huts of Son Trang. They all were dead, and they all were women and children. And the Marine Corps did not want

Son Trang 4 to do to them what My Lai had done to the Army. All members of the squad were arrested. The team leader was charged with premeditated murder.

And now, State Senator Gene Stipe from Peaceable Mountain out south of McAlester in southeastern Oklahoma was visiting with a kid from Calvin in the peanut country in the western edge of his Senate district. But they were standing outside a Quonset hut in Da Nang, Vietnam, and his constituent was that team leader charged with premeditated murder, and a military court was assembling inside the Quonset hut.

"You just need to prepare for the inevitable, Randy."

Gene had followed the My Lai case closely, and it was partly because of Hayden Donahue. Traveling the country together back in the 50s, looking for models on which to restructure Oklahoma's mental health programs, Hayden had talked endlessly of this black thing of the mind. He had seen it, he said, on the World War II battlefields of North Africa. He had learned there that prolonged combat butchers the minds of the winners as well as bodies of the losers. He had probed into the psyches of ruined men, and inside their heads had been eye-witness to the atrocities done to their own souls. After a man has been in the jungle or the desert or the bush for months, he said, seeing close friends killed by somebody out there he cannot see, facing the possibility of his own death at the same hands, the lines inside his mind begin to blur. He comes to live on the very sharpest edge of his nerves, ready to explode at any moment. And that explosion can be a heroic action that saves his life and the lives of others. Or it can be murder that sends him to prison for life. Sometimes, a man has no way to know the difference until after he has done it, and it has been assessed by men like those gathering in the Quonset now. And that is why Gene had dropped all that he was doing and volunteered to become defense counsel for Marine

Lance Corporal Randall D. Herrod when he read that the Calvin boy had been charged with premeditated murder.

Da Nang was chilling. Even at 110 degrees. Randy Herrod was accused of lining up the women and children of the village of Son Trang 4 with the cold, vengeful intent of shooting them where they stood. The soldier Schwartz, who had been grazed by a bullet and his rifle butt shattered by machinegun fire, already had been sentenced to 12 consecutive life sentences, one for each of the civilians he was found guilty of helping to murder without provocation. The rifle with the shattered stock that would prove the men were fired on was mysteriously missing from a Marine Corps ordnance obsessed with not losing weapons. All records of the rifle were gone. Witnesses who might have helped had been scattered among distant units. Some claimed they had been threatened with damage to their careers if they testified for Herrod. The Marines refused permission to visit Son Trang 4 – the murder scene if the charges were true. But, what bothered Gene about Da Nang was more than the sum total of all that.

The prosecutor, a colonel from the Judge Advocate General's office, was a big, heavy guy, and he appeared bewildered that Gene would question his procedures. There was a sense almost of ritual with a predestined end. They had already convicted the soldier Schwartz with the same evidence they would use against Herrod.

Everything went through the chain of command for approval. If the lower echelon didn't think the head man would approve something, they would fix it to where they thought he would approve. Command influence was built so deeply into the system that even the judicial process could not escape it. And all the other players were on their home court. Gene was a visitor. A guest.

He decided to break their stride a bit. Let them know it wasn't – at least – going to be routine. He began to file motions for them to furnish different things. Discovery. Made himself a nuisance.

The judge was named St. Johns. He was a pretty good judge. Gene found out the names of some men who had been in the military with him, learned about him, developed a little rapport with him. Gene filed a motion to transfer the case to the United States for trial. It was denied.

Back in Washington, he moved on all fronts. He talked with Speaker of the House Carl Albert, trying to get him to use his influence to get at least a change of location for the trial. Albert put him in touch with Mendel Rivers, powerful chairman of the Armed Services Committee, the man who decided what branch of service got how much money. But the Marines were dug in. The trial would stay in Da Nang. Gene filed an action in the Court of Military Appeals to transfer the trial to the United States. It didn't work. The Army was trying Lieutenant Calley in the United States, and they were catching all kinds of flack. Protesters marching. Hell-raising all the time. One of the Marine lawyers argued that with success.

When Gene got back to Oklahoma, he called a press conference and told Oklahomans about the kid from Oklahoma's peanut country, and the story went onto the national wires and became a part of the turbulent history of the U.S. in Vietnam. Gene filed an appeal to the United States Supreme Court, and the court refused it. So he went back to Da Nang for trial. He had felt the atmosphere changing with each trip he made. First time he went over, they treated him with great courtesy. Made sure he had sheets for his bunk, the amenities of living. Second time wasn't quite as good. Third time, damn, they didn't give him any linens at all.

He had assembled a defense team: Harry Palmer, a corporate lawyer in Oklahoma. He would help direct the trial so that it would cover all the grounds for a successful appeal. Dick Miller. He would search the law books for whatever rulings and precedents Gene needed. Senator Denzil Garrison, minority leader of the State

Senate, a friend who went along. All voluntary. Pay your own way. Their skills were weighted toward building an appeal from the conviction Gene feared was coming down.

On arrival, Gene picked up the Stars and Stripes military newspaper, and the headline was "Judge Banished From Country." St. Johns was no longer hearing the Herrod case. And then, the defense team's investigation uncovered official inside Marine correspondence that contained the assurance that Marine Lance Cpl. Randall D. Herrod would be found guilty of premeditated murder. And that is when Gene called the boy aside and told him to get ready for the verdict.

"Some cases are meant to be won at trial, Randy," he said, "and some on appeal. This case is going to be won on appeal."

After the trial started, the team would gather at night and discuss the case. Even Gene had to agree it was going better than anybody had dared hope. For the only time he could remember, he began to hope his assessment had been wrong.

Marine Lieutenant Oliver North took leave time and came to try to help the kid who had saved his life by covering his unconscious form with his own body in a firefight in the demilitarized zone. North sneaked into Son Trang 4 and measured off a map for Gene to use as an exhibit. They found a man who heard the sounds of the battle from base camp: "Yes, sir, I heard Viet Cong machine gun fire followed immediately by our rifle fire."

Herrod's team didn't have a machine gun.

They found a patrol leader who led his men into Son Trang days later and was ambushed by Viet Cong guerrillas, seventy yards from the village. They captured an American-made M-60 machinegun.

The combat-fresh reconnaissance officer whose report had triggered the whole investigation had been through his own ambushes by the time he took the witness stand. He said the same thing he had said in his report, but he said it in the way of a man who had been through what the boy had been through. And it came out sounding different.

Gene drew from Vietnamese women who were there that night the fact that Son Trang was a Viet Cong stronghold and that women participated in the killing, and that the men had been there that night, in the hut as the patrol approached. But, to have any hope of winning, they needed a coup d' grace. Somebody needed to explain what happens to a man out there. How people who have been in battle a long time begin to lose their guidance systems. Their stabilizers. How it changed their thinking.

Gene sat there, remembering his talks with Hayden Donahue. When Hayden had been in the military, he had done an extensive study on battle fatigue, and he had written a paper on what he discovered. The Air Force had paid for it. It gave him the kind of special credentials which were exactly what the Herrod defense team needed. And, the gentle little guy from the other side of Peaceable Mountain had by this time accumulated the prestige to put force behind what he said. Gene had gone with him to the ceremony the first time he was inaugurated as national president of the American Association of Psychiatry. Gene jumped up, suddenly, from the table and hurried out into the darkness.

They didn't show much light in Da Nang at night because the Viet Cong were always just out there in the dark, waiting to drop a mortar shell amid the plates on a table. No outdoor lighting at all. Gene made his way to a telephone and stood in line with the servicemen, waiting his turn. Finally, he reached Hayden Donahue at his home in Oklahoma City.

"What? Gene? Is that you? Where are you again? You want me to do what?"

He was the perfect witness. A kindly old country doctor, brushing back the white hair and looking out at the court with eyes gentled even further by popbottle glasses. Telling them eye to eye the

Hayden H. Donahue, the perfect witness

atrocities he had seen done to the minds of men who had been forced to deal with death too long. With a wistful kind of sadness. Making them feel it inside their own heads.

"Dr. Donahue? How would you say a combat veteran acts at such a point?"

"He acts instinctively rather than reasonably."

"And do you think it's possible, given Randy Herrod's time in combat and what he'd been through, that he was suffering from battle fatigue?"

"I would say it was more than possible. I would say it was likely."

"Would you say your opinion would be beyond dispute?"

There was that wry, lopsided smile.

"It wouldn't have been beyond dispute if I had seen him that night. But I know what a fighting man's limits are. They don't change that much from war to war."

Randy Herrod watched in awe:

At the beginning of the trial, Gene had sent us all over Da Nang looking for a yellow legal pad.

"I've never taken notes in the years I've practiced law," he said, "but since we're trying a case we're sure to appeal, I'm going to keep a record along the way – just in case. That way I'll know what to include in the summation."

Denny winked at me, then turned to Gene.

"Well," he said, "it's summation time. Let's take a look at your notes."

Denny reached across the table, picked up the yellow pad, and held it up for the rest of our team to see. On the first page were the words" TRIAL OF RANDY HE...."
That was all.

Everybody laughed, and we went to chow joking about Gene's lack of preparation.

Then it was time. Last chance for a verdict of innocent.

Speaking for more than two hours, Gene went through every item introduced into evidence, every single witness, and every bit of testimony. He didn't make a mistake on any of the factual matters, he didn't forget even a minor detail, and he didn't mispronounce one of the Vietnamese names used during the trial.

Then there was nothing to do but wait. Finally, it came:

"We, the members of this court-martial board find Lance Corporal Randall Herrod not guilty of all charges and specifications listed herein."

It filtered slow as morning sunshine into the stunned boy's head. No appeal. No more brig. He was going home. Oklahoma. They celebrated, of course. As well as they could in Da Nang, South Vietnam. Gene and Hayden were trying to get to their quarters from the officers' club. The night was solid black. Hayden couldn't see at all, so Gene went ahead leading him. Denny brought up the rear. Gene disappeared. Hayden stood there in the dark, feeling around.

"Gene? Where did you go?"

He could hear Denny giggling.

"Down here, Hayden."

Gene was trying to scramble out of a twelve-foot shellhole.

Hayden waited until they reached the door of their quarters.

"Gene," he said, "you may be a pretty good country lawyer, but you're one hell of a tour guide."

Then the boy called his grandfather, but he was not at home. He was, friends told the boy, riding the fire truck up and down the streets of Calvin, blowing the siren, telling everybody in town his grandson was innocent. As his grandfather had known he was.

"Just tell him," the boy said, "I'm coming home."

To Peanut Country. Oklahoma. Hughes County. The red-sandy banks of the Canadian River.

Gene appealed Sergeant Schwartz's 12 consecutive life sentences, and they were set aside. And that boy went home, too. Talked with his grandfather.

Randy tried to explain it to the townfolk of Calvin.

"Gene said he came because he believed in his responsibility to serve the people of his senatorial district – and he said I was one of those people."

It's what neighbors do, son.

36

The Fifth Marine

Fragging is a brutal sport. Or, at least, the United States Marines at one time became terribly afraid it would become so in Vietnam. The term fragging stems from the word fragmentation. Word scholars have never determined for certain whether the name derives from the fragmentation grenade that – when blended with a touch of battle-induced insanity – constitutes the only necessary equipment for fragging, or whether it comes from what the grenade does to the person upon whom it is used. It is, they agree, equally applicable to both.

Fragging is a thing that was done, sometimes, back unknowing deep in the bush in Vietnam and to a lesser degree in earlier wars. Once in World War II when a lieutenant who was supposed to be leading his men into the deadly rattling din of small arms fire froze and lay trembling like a boy in a shellhole, a hard-jawed Marine placed an armed hand grenade in the hole with him, and the rest of them moved out.

But men who were there said fragging reached its bloody peak in Vietnam. It was done often enough or tried often enough or at least talked about often enough that it entered the language. When word of it came home from the war, it spawned dark computer games to be played by those who were not there to know the bone-splintering fear and the insane dark hatreds that fear spawned in the souls of men killing too young and for too long.

The dictionary says fragging is "to wound or kill (a fellow soldier) by throwing a grenade or similar explosive at the victim." In the words of those who would do it, it is practiced when "certain career-motivated personnel have to be disciplined by the enlisted men." Sometimes, the "discipline" would start with a riot-control gas grenade that would burn the offending party's eyes and sear his mucous membranes. Just to show him how easily the real thing could be done. If he didn't straighten up, it was the fragmentation grenade or claymore mine.

When Vietnam was not violently painful or filled with incredible fear, one soldier tried to explain, it was such a crashing bore that a young man couldn't stand it. Somebody would bring out some marijuana, and they would huddle together with that special intimacy and fill in the hours between their killing chores with tales of bravado. And, too often, the talk would drift around to fragging. It struck fear into the hearts of men who were supposed to be unacquainted with it.

"One evening I had to awaken one of my officers. He was sleeping with a .45 pistol in his hand. I asked him about it.

"'I'm your headquarters commandant,' I told him. 'I'm not going to let the zips slip up on you in your hooch.'

"'I'm not afraid of the zips,' he said, 'I'm afraid of the troops.'"

About the time Randy Herrod and Gene and Harry Palmer and Dick Miller were sweating in front of that jury of Army officers in the Quonset hut at Da Nang, some kids about Herrod's age were sitting around in the Vietnam backbush, talking about how much they disliked their company commander, who slept now on his officer's cot only a few feet away in his hooch. Somebody brought out some marijuana, and they passed it around, and they talked some more about their captain and how the war sucked. And somebody mentioned fragging. And in that strange time in that strange place amid the soothing smog of marijuana, it came to sound like a thing to do. And before sanity could return, the straw was drawn, the clinch pin pulled, the wrist flicked, and the fragmentation grenade rolled off a practiced palm and bounced only once on the slatted wooden pallets of the tent floor before stopping precisely beneath the thin canvas of the cot on which the company commander slept. And the whole world came apart.

After Gene got back home from clearing Randy Herrod of murder charges, he got a telephone call from a family down at Norman. Their boy, they said, had been involved in some kind of incident called a fragging. Knowing he knew of military justice, they asked Gene if he would check into it. Look after their boy in that awful place over there. Here is what Gene found:

Four young men had been identified as those directly involved in rolling a grenade under the cot of their sleeping company commander, and they had been convicted – with the help of a fifth young Marine who testified against them – and sentenced to life imprisonment in Portsmouth for premeditated murder. All through the trial, and even after the conviction and sentencing, all four of the convicted Marines kept insisting that one of the four was innocent. That he had been wrongly convicted. That the fifth young Marine who testified actually was among the four who did the fragging. The young Marine Captain who prosecuted the case heard it so often that he couldn't quit hearing it even after he won his case and was discharged back to the United States to try to resume some kind of normal life. He kept hearing, even in his sleep, those men insist that he had sent one innocent young Marine to Portsmouth prison for life. Trying to find some peace, he went back to Vietnam and insisted that they reopen the investigation.

The Marines put the Fifth Marine under the care of a military psychiatrist, and at the psychiatrist's urging, the young man confessed that he had been the lookout for the fragging, and yes, there was an innocent man serving a life sentence in Portsmouth. He had been so terribly frightened…

The psychiatrist reported to the court that he had obtained the confession they wanted and turned the confession over to them for use in a trial against the young man who had helped them convict the other four. They bound him, too, over for trial for murder. It was that fifth young Marine whose family called Gene and asked him to go back to Vietnam and see what was happening to their boy.

Gene went through the now-familiar process of arranging a trip to Vietnam to see him, but before he could leave, the Marines moved the case to Okinawa, Da Nang having lost some of its luster as a trial site after Gene's success in the Randy Herrod case. Gene visited with the boy and filed his usual motion to transfer the trial back to the United States. This time, they granted it. To Camp Pendleton in California. It looked at the beginning like an easy, open-and-shut kind of case. Everybody with any knowledge of the law at all knew confessions to a priest or lawyer or doctor – surely your psychiatrist – were confidential and therefore inadmissible as evidence against you at trial. But the military court kept over-ruling motions to throw out the confession as evidence.

Gene set out to find something in military law that would make a confession to the psychiatrist inadmissible, and he couldn't find it. But he did find a provision that said, in effect, if you were going to use such a statement against a Marine, you had to tell him in advance. Give him right to counsel. And so forth. A sort of military

Miranda. They had not followed that procedure with the Fifth Marine. Gene raised that question, and when he was able to cite military law, the judge threw it out. Disallowed the confession.

There are, as has been said, basic differences in military law and civilian law. Some cut to a defense attorney's advantage and some cut against him. Military justice, for example, is inflexible. Rigid to the point of breaking. That inflexibility had almost sent Randy Herrod to prison for life. Gene spent hours thinking about it. Could the military's own inflexibility be turned against it?

Although the confession was all the evidence the military had against the Fifth Marine, and the confession had been thrown out, the military refused to dismiss the case. Nobody would admit they had made a mistake. Investigating officers whose testimony had sent an innocent man to Portsmouth for life refused to change their statements, even in the face of a confession that contradicted them. And, Gene mused, if everybody testified in the Fifth Marine's trial as they had at the first trial, then the young Marine still would be an innocent witness in the eyes of the jury despite his confession to the contrary. In order to convict the Fifth Marine, somebody had to admit an error. And nobody would. Fear of fragging had caused the Marine Corps to send their top-name investigators into this case, and now all of them stood firm. Gene had his case laid out for him. He subpoenaed for the defense all the prosecution witnesses from the original trial.

The defense had the option of trying the case before a panel of enlisted men or trying it to a panel of officers. Despite the fact that his client had confessed to being involved in an incident that killed a company commander, Gene asked for a panel of officers. Every one of the six who were chosen – a full colonel, a light colonel, two majors, two captains had been company commanders. One still was. It looked to the casual eye like an impossible jury. But Gene was coming to understand military law: By the time a man becomes an officer with hopes of a brilliant career, he has become so steeped in the military system he will follow the rules to the death. Or to an acquittal of a confessed co-fragger.

At trial, all witnesses from the previous trial testified precisely as they had in the first trial and the confessed co-fragger was acquitted and sent back home to a normal world. Gene's conscience got to bothering him. Not because he had gotten a man acquitted who had confessed, but because it had left an innocent young Marine serving out his life in Portsmouth.

Gene filed an appeal. Its primary thrust was the confession of guilt from a client for whom Gene had won a ruling of innocent. The military – following their rules without blinking – released the innocent Marine from prison and sent him home, too.

37

J.I.: The Rest of the Story

The biographer of Thomas Jefferson said, "A passion for politics stems usually from an insatiable need, either for power, or for friendship and adulation, or a combination of both."

In McAlester in 1972, it stemmed from a need for a friendly place to play dominoes, and it was kindled in the hearts of some coal-mining farmers grown too old to farm or to mine coal. It bloomed with particular heat in the heart of J.I. Stipe. Being always too busy trying to scrape out a living with his hands, J.I. had never had the time to get really into the finer art of politics and thus had been forced to practice it as it was meant to be practiced instead of what it has become. He had never asked anything from politics except decent schools for his kids, maybe, and a good sheriff to look after the safety of his family and a good county commissioner to do what was right by the roads and such. Jacob Irvine Stipe was just a good man, and he always tried to believe that other men were, too, but he had always wanted the structure in place to see that those less inclined to be so, also were good men. He had always expected good treatment from his government and had always gotten it except for that time back in the 1930s when Alfalfa Bill Murray sent the National Guard down from Oklahoma City and took him off the picket line and put him in prison for the night.

By 1972, J.I. had gotten too old to make a living digging holes for utility posts or digging coal from the deep mines, and too old to indulge in his hobby of hitting a baseball so far a fielder had to go into forever to get it. And the Social Security Law President Roosevelt signed back in 1935 had evolved to where J.I. had himself a little pension, his boys were gone, and he lived in town with Rose, his second wife, and there wasn't a whole lot to do. So, he started playing dominoes just about every day down at the city hall with buddies of similar ages and histories and inclinations. There'd be, oh, eight, ten, sometimes as many as 15 to 20 such men gather up at the City Hall and play dominoes. And talk about how it had been to dig coal from the deep mines, and what a man Peter Hanraty was, and how dirty it was of Bill Murray to pull them off the picket line and put them in prison overnight.

The city manager and the city council decided it didn't look good having those old men loafing around City Hall while official city business was being conducted. So they banned them. And the old gang was left not only with no coal to mine, no crops to hoe, and no kids to raise, but no place to play dominoes and talk about all the other things. When they would meet on the street they would talk about how they had always thought that the City Hall belonged to the people, and how some people went there to pay their water bills and some went there to the council meetings, and some went there to play dominoes. And if they weren't hurting anybody or getting in the way, they ought to be able to play dominoes at City Hall. Or somewhere.

J.I. got to remembering how he had helped elect board members at Cooper School and county sheriffs and commissioners and how much more likely they had been to listen to what he had to say if he had had a hand in putting them where they were. So, at age 75, J.I. became a politician. He and his buddies organized, and they put themselves together a complete new slate of city government candidates – top to bottom – making sure none of them would object to some old coal-mining farmers playing dominoes down at City Hall. They canvassed McAlester. While the city government of McAlester was busying itself with what it saw as the important issues of the day, the old-timers were circulating through town politicking the way they used to politic when they were young and wanted to be sure somebody was there to help look after their families. At the next election a bewildered mayor and city council learned it was they – and not the old men – who had been turned out of City Hall. The old-timers elected their whole ticket. And the new city administration shared the old men's view that it would be a good thing if older McAlester residents had a place to gather and play dominoes or anything else that they wanted to do.

Ernest Albert's boy, Carl, by then speaker of the United States House of Representatives, helped them get a federal grant, and the J.I. Stipe Recreation Center was dedicated Thursday, March 27, 1975. It was a big deal. Had a swimming pool and a gymnasium and a cafeteria. J.I. tried to talk them out of it, naming it after him. He didn't want any fuss and bother, only a place to play dominoes in peace. But they did it, anyway.

And when construction was completed, there was a room especially set aside for men too old to dig coal anymore to gather and play dominoes. Some tried to say that J.I.'s influential state-senator son, Gene, was behind it, but J.I. always grinned that grin when he heard that. His blackheaded boy had been supporting the city administration J.I. had turned out of office. But, sometimes, politics just wouldn't follow family lines. After all, Gene had taken a job helping Johnston Murray back in '51, even after the Murray boy's daddy had locked J.I. up in the prison for a night.

Gene's collection of people stories had, by the 1970s, grown to include every conceivable kind of character. He's telling another. Listen:

This old boy came in to see me one noon. He had been to cosmetology school and opened up a beauty shop. He was obviously homosexual, you know, he had all the attributes. He had a crazy name like Berkhoid, or something, not a common name, didn't appeal to any-body. He'd grown up here in McAlester. I'd helped him get his cosmetology license. He opened up a shop, but women in McAlester wouldn't come to him.

"What you need is a bigger market, Berkhoid. You need to jazz your deal up. You need to call yourself some-thing else. No one wants to call you by that name. No one's ever been famous with that name. Call yourself Mr. Charles or something.

"Maybe a bigger city, like Tulsa, Oklahoma City. They don't care if you're gay up there or not. Matter of fact if you kinda put yourself out a little bit, they may just love you. You ought to maybe serve a little wine or cock-tails or something."

That old boy was one of the very few ever known to follow my advice.

He left town, went to Tulsa. I made a talk to the Junior League up there a little while later, and they were all excited, talking about getting their appointment with Mr. Charles. Mr. Charles was serving drinks and, durn, it got me curious about it, and, sure enough, I went by and it was old Berkhoid or whatever. He had people on the waiting list for two months. Those gals in the junior league were bartering around, trading. If one had an appointment she could trade it for something else. Everybody wanted to see Mr. Charles. Mr. Charles had already hired him several other beauty operators so he was doing good. He was making lots of money. Those Junior League gals really thought he was something.

❖

"Your husband will be a dead man come Friday."

That, Judge Luther Bohanon's wife insisted, was what the man had said. On the telephone. That is what she told her husband when he arrived at home from work that day to find her quite distraught.

"Your husband will be a dead man come Friday."

It summed up the bitterness of the decade since Luther Bohanon had taken over supervision of the integration of the Oklahoma City School District.

In 1964, the Oklahoma City School Board had offered to assign students, faculty and staff to neighborhood schools without regard to race. But, that couldn't work because the neighborhoods that supplied children to the schools were segregated, first by state laws and later by discrimination by realtors and financial institutions. School segregation in Oklahoma City had been so rigidly enforced, it had helped to segregate the neighborhoods. By 1972, It had become clear there was no other solution, and Bohanon approved a student assignment plan designed to ensure the integration of students. The board protested that it would require busing children, both black and white, far from their neighborhood schools. Bohanon ordered them to do it, anyway. And that was when the fight had turned brutal.

Luther Lee Bohanon had seen representations of his own image hanging from street overpasses. Furious Oklahoma Cityans had paraded with picket signs that called him everything from a Nazi to a Communist. Stickers on cars ahead of him when he drove to work in the morning read "Bus Bohanon." The FBI had been called in to protect Mrs. Bohanon. Some things happened that shamed even the judge: a 14-year-old boy was taken into custody by a federal marshal for going to the wrong school. Hurtful things. Young children sent by bus to strange new schools clear across town from their mothers. But what was being done had to be done.

"You either have the courage," he kept telling himself, "or you don't."

Calling upon knowledge gathered in the rough old days in the oil fields of Seminole, he reassured his wife:

"If a fellow is gonna kill you, he's not going to tell you about it."

38

A Sick Kitten for Mr. Rader

The University of Oklahoma Health Sciences Center – operated and funded by the Oklahoma University Board of Regents – was in trouble. The center was contained in a few square blocks of old red-brick buildings and converted houses in eastern Oklahoma City. There was a medical school and two hospitals – University and Crippled Children's – about 400 medical students and a few interns and residents. A medical star or two were there, like organ transplant pioneer Dr. Rainey Williams, but there was little in the way of an organized medical community. The hospitals primarily took care of indigent patients, some welfare recipients from the rural areas, and some who were dumped on the state institution from local private hospitals. The College of Medicine was about to lose its accreditation. An outside consultant was brought in to see if he could get things back into proper order. After a quick survey, he reported in.

"Hey," he told the state Senate, "we can't do any consulting over here, we are just trying to keep the doors open from one day to the next."

It had become habit, at such times, to look to Mr. Rader. Through the years, his genius at handling the sales tax money had grown. With unfettered freedom to transfer funds and manipulate accounts, Mr. Rader had discovered that if you had a federally approved state plan and submitted it early, you could estimate what federal funds were going to be needed for the upcoming quarter of the year, and you could draw that federal money in advance. He figured out he could then take that federal money and put it in the state treasury and it became state money, and he could take that state money and use it as more matching funds to lure in still more federal dollars. And that was one of the ways in which Mr. Rader worked his magic. And they knew that in Washington. But they knew Mr. Rader, what he did with the money, and it was hard for them to tell him he was not going to get it.

And the state legislature figured the same thing could happen to the Crippled Children's Hospital, so they transferred it to Mr. Rader's department of state government – which by now had had so many things transferred to it that it had been renamed the Oklahoma Department of Institutions, Social and Rehabilitative Services.

Improve Crippled Children's, they said. Enlarge, build and equip it. Do whatever it is that you do. Mr. Rader went over to see what he was taking on, and suddenly the project became much more than just another agency transfer. Here is what he found:

Doctors refused to operate in Children's Hospital if oxygen was involved because it was so dangerous it might explode. Services that they had delivered had gone unbilled for months, so there was no cash flow. The hospital's credit rating was so bad it could not get supplies unless the money was paid at the time supplies were picked

Lloyd Rader and Vera Alder, a legendary team.

up. Frustrated employees said people had carried off what operating equipment there was. The nurses had nothing to work with. The doctors had no tools. Someone, they said, had even taken the Isolettes for newborn babies. The companion adult hospital, University, had nothing to handle the babies with, and no one to pay for it, and they were in about the same financial shape as Children's. Nurses were trying to do the best they could with the heartbreaking little that they had. Nobody really knew what to do when a desperately ill little Oklahoma baby was sent to the hospital for help.

Deeply touched, Mr. Rader moved out of his office and over to the hospital, turning much of the day-to-day running of the welfare department to a handful of people he knew he could trust: Vera Alder who had been there when he got there, and Pauline Mayer and Lowell Green, who had all come up the hard way and understood such things. Mr. Rader set up a "brain trust" of welfare department heads that met every Monday morning and discussed department problems as they developed. If one had a problem, maybe another had a solution, or maybe somebody else knew something, and it was just a round robin. Everybody had input. And all of them had been trained to their work by Lloyd Rader, and had they not thought about such things the way Lloyd Rader thought about them, they would have been gone long before. Necessity erased petty differences. The crisis and Mr. Rader's all-out assault on it closed them in. They combined themselves into a CEO, and the welfare department ran, almost, as if Mr. Rader was there. He left signed stationery with Vera, and he'd dictate to her over the phone and she would fit it into what space was appropriate on the letterhead and go on from there. When something came up that they had to talk to him, they had to go to the hospital and wait, sometimes, for three or four hours to get to see him. Lloyd Rader was wheeling and dealing at his best. Dark to dark. He was going to give Oklahoma a Children's Hospital to be proud of.

When a sick baby was brought into the hospital and surgery was indicated and the hospital didn't have the necessary equipment, Mr. Rader would send a truck overnight to Texas to get the equipment. Race it back to Oklahoma in order for surgery to be performed the next day. Pledge his life to pay for it. Freeze complaining bureaucrats with that blue-ice stare. Tell them that when a child needs surgery, there is no time for purchase orders and bids. And he took the heat. Finally, things started straightening out. Mr. Rader sent over one of his good secretaries to be the administrator's secretary. DISRS started paying the bills on time, and Mr. Rader gradually began going back to his old office in the Sequoyah Building.

He finished up the new hospital building and built another new one and built a rehabilitation unit for autistic children. By then he had assembled a medical staff, and they stayed because they knew they were finally going to get something to work with, and they were going to have a decent place to work. Children's Hospital was on its way from a disgrace to being something Oklahoma could be proud of.

Vera, who could do such things, faced Mr. Rader, with a cryptic warning: "They've given us the kitten (Children's Hospital)," she said, "don't let them give us the old cat (University Hospital for adults), too."

It would, she knew, be the financial straw that broke their backs.

39

Constitution Doesn't Stop at the Prison Gate

Judge Luther Bohanon's effigy had hardly stopped turning slowly in the wind from Oklahoma City overpasses when it happened.

At 2:20 p.m. on July 27, 1973, between twenty-five and thirty inmates at the McAlester State Prison seized guards in the mess hall. Within minutes, six hundred prisoners were involved. Prison buildings were burning. The prison yard was in the hands of the rioters. An evil column of smoke boiled up that some said could be seen for 40 miles. Lawyers were inside taking depositions from prisoners on conditions some had predicted would lead to just such a riot.

Oklahoma Highway Patrol, Army and Air National Guard units rushed to reinforce prison personnel. Four state officials – Chairman of the State Board of Corrections Irvine Ungerman, Director of the Department of Corrections Leo McCracken,

Commissioner of Public Safety Wayne Lawson, Prison Warden Park Anderson – worked through a night haunted by strange, uncontrolled shouting, dread and loathing, muffled explosions like distant thunder, fear and humidity that popped sweat on foreheads. Sullen red flickers of flames brought no light. There was an undefined, urgent feeling that whatever it was the justice system was supposed to restrain was about to be loosed into the world. There was one man at work that few knew or were told about. His name was Wade Watts, ex-gambler, preacher. President of the Oklahoma NAACP. Direct lineal successor to Roscoe Dunjee. Here is how he would remember it:

I was the assistant chaplain out there, and I had just left out when the riot started. They sent me a notice that they were having a riot out there, and they had 26 hostages. That night, we talked them out of all the hostages but 11. The next day Ed Hardy came down as a spokesman for Governor Hall, and Attorney General Larry Derryberry came down, and Gene. And Gene, he told me – I was the chief negotiator between the convicts and them – "don't promise em nothing." And I didn't promise em nothing. And all they wanted was the newsmen to come in there, and the television men and the radio men. The media was what they was asking for, and they said, "We'll release the hostages." And I would go back and tell them and they refused to send the newsmen in there. Anyway, they finally asked the convicts this: "Would you all exchange" – they still had eleven in there including assistant warden Johnston – "would you exchange the hostages for Rev. Watts?" They said, "Yeah, we'll exchange em for Rev. Watts." And I was going to exchange, you know. I told Wayne Lawson, let me call the governor. And Lawson, he said, let me talk to him, too. So he got the phone and he walked about 25 yards from where I was at. When he got through talking, he slammed the phone down and said this damned old phone quit working. Well, what I was wanting to talk with the governor about was not to release no fire on us like they did at Attica.

(Two years earlier, Attica Correctional Facility at Attica, N.Y., was the scene of the bloodiest one-day encounter between Americans since the Indian massacres of the late nineteenth century. Inmates of the overcrowded Attica prison took over the cell blocks and killed several trusty guards. Thirty-nine inmates were killed and more than 80 wounded in the 15 minutes it took for state police to retake the prison. Total death toll was 43.)

I didn't want nothing like that, so when he slammed the phone down, I backed out. I said, "No I won't exchange myself. You got the stuff in there to bargain with. I wouldn't be no bargaining power for you."

Old Ed Hardy told some of the biggest lies you ever heard. Ed Hardy, he said this, "We carried em some hot biscuits out there and some meatloaf and they said, 'By god, we don't want no meatloaf, we want steaks.'" They hadn't had anything to eat for two or three days. They would have eaten anything they could a got a hold to. Whenever the convicts wanted me to see something bad, they would pretend like they wanted prayer. One old boy, his toilet stool had busted, that old stuff running out in the floor. He said, "Rev. Watts?" He said, "See if you can get them to send a plumber down here and fix this."

And I went out and told em and they said, "You go back down there and ask him if he checked out the accommodations before he come down here."

I went down there one morning and that gas was stinging my eyes, burning my nose, eyes running water, nose too, I guess that was the shortest prayer I ever delivered. I got out of there and I went by the front office and I said, "Those boys want you all to send them some fans down there and blow that gas off."

"That's a damn lie, ain't nobody gassed em."

They gassed one old boy to death. They turned that gas loose, killed one of them. They told me they said, "Rev. Watts the only way we could breathe was just get down and put our nose at the bottom of the door."

I got a lot of experience out of that. What it is, they are scared. The guards that was out there with me, they was all scared. I didn't have no gun or ammunition or anything, but I wasn't scared because I had the respect of the convicts. And I wasn't afraid of the convicts, I was afraid of the prison administration.

Finally, they decided to let the newsmen go in there. See, and they told me to go tell them that we gonna let the newsmen in there and I went and told em. They released the hostages when they said they would let the newsmen in there. They didn't tell me they had told the newsmen not to talk to any of the convicts, or record anything they was saying. And when they went in there, they couldn't say nothing. Then the convicts thought I had betrayed em. But I hadn't, cause they didn't tell me that they had done told em not to talk.

It took a massive show of force, including use of tear gas, and another seven days before all prisoners were again confined to their cells. The prison was little more than a smoldering ruin. Damage was estimated at twenty million dollars. Four prisoners were dead and forty others, inmates and guards, were injured.

The reason the lawyers were in the prison taking depositions when the riot began was that Judge Luther Bohanon had before him a case he was studying named Battle v. Anderson. The

Anderson was Park, warden of the prison. Battle was an African-American convict serving time for robbery. His primary redeeming social value was that his anti-social actions had put him inside the walls of Big Mac where he could see equally anti-social actions coming back at the inmates.

The Oklahoma State Penitentiary was built with convict labor, beginning in 1908 at the insistence of Kate Barnard, the world's first woman to be elected to a statewide office. Nicknamed Oklahoma's Angel of Mercy, she brought Oklahoma convicts home on a special train through a snowstorm from the horrors of Kansas' underground coal mines where they had been leased out as laborers. Oklahoma housed them in a field surrounded by electrified barbed wire and they built themselves a new prison. Kate naively saw it as an indication of how well Oklahoma would treat its prisoners in the future.

But, "Big Mac," as it had come to be known, had done little but deteriorate. By the 1970s, it was a mixture of the Middle Ages and 1930s motion-picture stereotype, described by those who knew as one of the most "inefficient, archaic and corrupt" prisons in the nation, ruled with unmerciful discipline and brutal guards. Kept filled by a recidivism rate of 70 per cent.

In 1970, Big Mac's inmate population was 219 per cent of its intended capacity. Three and four prisoners occupied cells designed for one or two. Inmates slept in libraries, garages, stairwells and hallways. Rats roamed. The sewer didn't work right, and filth oozed into living areas. Mail was censored. Negroes and whites were seg-regated. Food was sickening. Punishment was isolation in the hole, a totally dark, windowless cell that contained only a toilet and a sink. Oklahoma imprisoned people at twice the rate of the rest of the nation, and held them half again as long. Warnings that an explosion was abuilding had long gone unheard.

In 1970, there was an especially senseless and severe beating of a convict. Battle witnessed it and led a rebellion in protest.

Hundreds of prisoners started a sitdown strike and refused to return to their cells. Battle and the others were put in solitary confinement for ninety days. Beatings grew more frequent. More severe. Battle and five other prisoners made up a petition, listing exact incidents. Asking for relief. Prison officials ignored it.

Attorneys for the American Civil Liberties Union (ACLU) helped Battle sculpt the heat and the filth and bad food and pain of a beating into words that fit the proper little niches of the judicial system: denial of constitutional and civil rights, cruel and unusual punishment, denial of the right of due process, equal protection under the laws, freedom of speech, religion, and assembly, redress of grievances, and access to the courts.

Thus translated sufficiently to pierce the high stone walls of prison, the suit was filed on April 24, 1972, against Warden Anderson and the Oklahoma Department of Corrections. And that was the case that was on the desk of U.S. District Court Judge Luther Lee Bohanon when the lid blew off Big Mac. He hardly had had time to read it. The case originally had been given to Judge Edwin Langley, chief judge of the Eastern District of Oklahoma. He suffered a heart problem, so with "Bus Bohanon" bumper stickers still weathering on the backs of Oklahoma cars, the case moved like a magnet to Oklahoma's most controversial federal judge.

With post-riot conditions worsening, the Battle trial began on March 14, 1974, before Judge Bohanon. The next day, Bohanon, unmellowed by his 72 years or his 13 years of school integration bitterness, announced from the bench that his decision was in favor of the inmates.

"Shameful!" He said. "Disgraceful! I had no idea until this week of the deep cruelty inmates were subjected to. Treatment is so shameful it is no wonder they commit the worst acts known to man."

And he drew up a long list of what the prison system had been doing that it would no longer do, and an even longer list of what it had not been doing that it would begin to do. His written opinion covered 60 legal-sized pages and contained 43 individual orders to corrections officials.

"If the Constitution doesn't work for prison inmates, racial minorities, the impoverished," Bohanon said, "it is of no value to anyone."

He would, he told prison officials, have regular hearings to see that they did what they were instructed to do.

40

World-Class Care in a Coal Mine Town

From the rise on which sits the J.I. Stipe Community Center in McAlester, you can see an assemblage of buildings off to the north. State Senator Gene Stipe loves to drive visitors past one of those buildings.

"I want you to look at this. Do you see all that green on the roof? That's copper. It started out copper color, and that's a beautiful thing to finish a building in. Look at that color now. Isn't that pretty?"

But it is what is inside the building that really moves him. It is the Carl Albert Community Mental Health Center. People in there go quietly about their task of bringing the cutting edge in modern mental health care to the southeastern Oklahoma coal town of McAlester.

Dr. Hayden Donahue built the first federally funded comprehensive mental health center in the United States within sight of the state hospital which he had rebuilt from a snakepit. That was in 1968. In 1974, the second comprehensive community mental health center in Oklahoma was built in McAlester, hometown of Senator Gene Stipe, the man who was responsible for Donahue being in Oklahoma. The McAlester center was the result of a three-way effort between Pittsburg Countians, Donahue, Gene, and the speaker of the U.S. House of Representatives.

"Mr. Speaker?" Hayden had said it in that warm and disarming way he had, peering through the pop-bottle glasses. "Surely you can help us with funding to build a facility to be called the Carl Albert Community Mental Health Center."

And that is how the cutting edge of mental health care happened to be in the southeastern Oklahoma coal town of McAlester. Folks from Peaceable Mountain don't have to go it alone like they did in 1936, and they do not have to be torn from their homes and institutionalized in Norman or Fort Supply or Vinita. The center reaches people in ten counties. Outreach centers are located in several of the area's small towns. They offer every kind of mental health help that the federal law authorizing it permits. Twenty-four hours a day, seven days a week. In folks' own community, or within 50 miles of it. That is why State Senator Gene Stipe, loves to drive visitors past.

"A caring place," he says. "So much better than anything we ever had before."

And, he casts a last look back over his shoulder at the green copper roofs.

"They do a heck of a job."

The two men, one black, one white, met at the doorway to the radio station in Moore. Stopped and stared, each knowing the other in an oddly intimate way, although neither had ever seen the other before. The appearance of neither lived up to the expectations of the other. Johnny Lee Clary had come prepared to face a young, smirking Negro with Angela Davis afro and poorly concealed switchblade knife. Before him stood an aging, white-headed black man with his preaching suit on. Grin crinkles around his eyes. Hand extended in greeting.

"Hello there, Mr. Clary, I been praying for you."

Clary quickly withdrew his hand. Stared at it.

"Don't worry, Mr. Clary, it won't come off."

Wade Watts had come to face a terrible apparition of the racist Old South whose evil had struck such fear into his home with its late night telephone calls and threatening letters. Before him stood a young white man with lively eyes, not very big, not very old, and having no appearance of evil.

"Okay, gentlemen, time to get this debate going."

Thus it was the first time the Imperial Wizard of the Ku Klux Klan in Oklahoma and the President of the National Association for the Advancement of Colored People of Oklahoma met face to face. Neither had arrived by an easy path.

Johnny Clary could remember skipping home from Sunday School singing, "Jesus loves the little children, All the children of the world; red and yellow black and white…"

Then thunder striking.

"Don't ever let me catch you singing words like that again!"

And that was the end of Sunday school for little Johnny Clary, born in Del City, Oklahoma, to a racist father and a mother who had created her own world with alcohol and drugs. The boy came home one night when he was 11 to find his father standing with a gun to his head. As he pleaded, his father pulled the trigger. Johnny Lee moved to California to live with his sister. The year he turned 18, he moved back to Oklahoma and joined the Ku Klux Klan and started his climb to the top of the organization.

Wade Watts had known, somehow, from the days when he had to step off the road to allow the schoolbus to pass carrying white children like Johnny Lee Clary that he would, someday, have to confront a Johnny Lee Clary. Almost like Clary's face had been pressed against the window of that bus. Wade did not know Clary, but he knew Clary's voice as did his wife and children from late-night phone calls, spewing hate. "Niggers!" Threatening terrible things. Calling down the residue of terror from ancestral blood-memories. The Imperial Wizard of the Ku Klux Klan in Oklahoma dearly loved to torment the president of the NAACP in Oklahoma.

Wade had tried to handle the Ku Klux Klan the way Jesus would.

"Clary sent some Ku Klux Klan down here to whip me one night, and they were eating down to Pete's Place. Pete was living at that time, and I made a deal with him that I would take care of their dinner. When they got through with dinner, I pulled my shirt off, stripped down to my waist and Pete took me in there.

"'Rev. Watts here has paid for your dinner,' Pete told them, 'and now he is ready for the whipping.'"

They couldn't do it.

Then the Ku Klux Klan announced plans to burn a 45-foot cross in a vacant lot next to Wade's house.

"They said there would be 25,000 or 30,000 people there. So I went into court with them. Their lawyer was Robert Shelton, old Grand Cyclops out of Tuskaloosa, Alabama. That trial lasted all day and the court finally decided that they couldn't burn the cross. Well, they marched anyway – around my house that night. I got a call from one of the deacons, and he said, 'Rev. Watts don't you come out. We believe this is a ploy, maybe, to kill you.' So I didn't go out. While some of them marched around my house, some of them set the church on fire. It burned about halfway, but the rest of it was all smoked up and messed up."

And all of that is why Wade had told the radio station he would be happy to meet the Imperial Wizard of the Klan face to face in a radio debate. And now the news director had his hand in the air and was counting, and it wasn't at all the way Wade had thought it was going to be.

The news director pointed. The red light went on.

"John, why does the Klan have an organization that they don't allow Negroes to join?"

"Because the Negroes have an organization they do not allow any white people to join, Reverend. It is called the NAACP."

"Mr. Clary. Back in 1909, in Abraham Lincoln's hometown in Illinois, there was two Negroes that was lynched. They found out the next day that both of them was innocent. The white people decided they'd get together and see that nothing like that ever happened again. Seven whites and two blacks got together and the organization they started back there is known to this day as the National Association for the Advancement of Colored People – the NAACP. About a fourth of our membership now is white."

Clary squirmed.

"Well, the Bible says everything ought to stay after its own kind. I don't believe in race mixing."

"Mr. Clary, you partly right. The Bible say that God made the fowls of the air after their kind, the beasts of the forest after their kind, the fish of the sea after their kind, but, see, he didn't make man after no kind. He said, 'Let Us make man in Our image and after Our likeness.'"

"Where do you find that at in the Bible?"

Wade hand-signaled his wife to go to the car and get his Bible. Showed Clary the scripture.

"Well, I don't believe in whites and Negroes going to church together."

"Well, Mr. Clary, in the 10th Chapter of Acts, there is this Phillip, a white man, joined in a chariot with a black man, an Ethiopian, and he converted this Ethiopian and this Ethiopian said, 'What doth hinder me from being baptized?'

"They stopped the chariot, Mr. Clary, and this white man carried the black man down there to the water, baptized him, and took him into the church right there, right then."

"Well, I don't believe in mixed marriages."

Wade flipped his Bible to the 12th chapter of Numbers. Tapped it with his finger.

"This, Mr. Clary, is where Moses married an Ethiopian woman. His sister, Miriam, spoke out against it, and God put leprosy on her for speaking out against it. Now, Mr. Clary, what do you think he'll do to you."

And so it went until the red light went off and they were no longer speaking to the residents of Moore. Clary was furious.

"Mr. Clary, come over here, please."

Wade walked over to where his wife stood with a baby in her arms.

"Mr. Clary, this is my little adopted daughter. Her mother was white; her father was black. The white side of the family didn't want the baby, the black side of the family said they wasn't able to take care of the baby. I asked them if they would give me the baby."

Wade pulled the blanket back from her face. She smiled, her little eyes shining as if she knew what her daddy was doing.

"Mr. Clary, how could you hate this baby? She ain't never done nothing to you."

Clary stormed out of the studio.

"Mr. Clary? You can't do enough to me, and you can't say enough about me to make me hate you. I love you like a brother."

Wade called it after him from the door of the studio.

Johnny Lee Clary did not look back.

41

Act Like Director, or You'll Be One

By 1978, Oklahoma was a nationwide model for community mental health centers. The system consisted of the three state mental hospitals, three state-run community mental health centers and five community mental health centers that were partially state supported, plus 33 satellite programs and 42 alcohol and drug treatment programs. This system had reduced the average patient stay at Central State to 25 days, compared with eight to ten years in 1958. Total census of the department's hospitals had been reduced from 8,620 in 1953 to about 3,000. And, yes, most all of it had been done under the direction of the man who said he never again would direct Oklahoma's mental health program.

Hayden Donahue had barely got settled in his new home as superintendent of Central State Hospital in Norman back in 1961 when House Speaker J.D. McCarty had called. McCarty wanted a mental health budget that he could trust. Donahue refused to write it. He was, he said, the superintendent of a state hospital, not the director of mental health. He had quit, remember?

McCarty, who seldom heard the word no, informed Donahue he would write the budget for the department as if he were director, or: "You will be the director."

In order to avoid the job, Donahue had written the budget. And so it had gone through the 1960s, Donahue serving officially as superintendent of Central State Hospital in Norman and unofficially as director of the Department of Mental Health, working with Dr. Al Glass, who was off and on director through that decade. Together, they had continued to pass milestones in the treatment of the mentally ill in Oklahoma.

They finally closed down the most racially segregated mental hospital in the United States, the one old Bill Murray had insisted on building at Taft so that white people who were insane wouldn't have to be with Negroes who were insane. Donahue established a complete mental health center for children, designed to begin treatment "back where the problems really begin." In 1970, he had relented and become the official director again. But, just as he had feared, success was turning on him again. By 1978, his theories again were working so well that he again became a target of some legislators who felt that the three main hospitals – in their districts – were being bled dry by the community-based treatment movement. Ever-increasing investigations were stepping up the level of stress. And Hayden Donahue was 65 years old and tiring. Drumming up continuing financing for the community mental health centers would require tremendous work.

"I think Oklahomans would support us if we could get our message out," he told close friends, "but I just don't have the energy, like I used to, to get in my car and head out to speak anywhere that I can draw a crowd."

In 1978, Hayden Hackney Donahue resigned for a second time as state mental health director. But, he agreed to remain as superintendent at Central State for another year. The legislature unanimously passed a bill creating the Hayden H. Donahue Mental

Health Institute, which would comprise all Norman mental health facilities. That included the former snake pit that had nauseated Donahue on his first day at work – and the first federally funded community mental health center in the nation.

At dedication ceremonies on December 2, 1978, Carl Albert said, "This is a great institution, but to build a building to reflect the character of the man, you would have to build it bigger than the Empire State Building."

Oklahoma State Senator Gene Stipe said Donahue educated the entire state, including the legislature, on the importance of community treatment. "Now," said a board member, "he's an institution."

As director of the Oklahoma Institute for Mental Health Education and Training, Donahue continued to teach and consult in the residency program at Central State Hospital.

And so, the gentle kid with pop-bottle glasses who came from the other side of Peaceable Mountain stepped down with a national reputation that could be matched by only one other living Oklahoman. And that Oklahoman, too, got to thinking about retiring that year.

Lloyd Rader, past age 70, had become a legend while he still was getting up every morning, draining that bad lung that started with the childhood fall from a horse, and working until well after dark. Six, seven days a week. And he did not slow. His wife, Ruth, made a mercy pact with his long-suffering workers that she would call him at 7 p.m. and remind him it was time to come home to dinner. After she died in 1975, they would watch him look up at the clock at 7, and when she did not call, he would turn back to work until his staff was too exhausted to go on.

He had taken the scandal-ridden little relief-check agency and turned it into a omnibus public assistance department that had a building of its own and a budget approaching $1 billion. It was universally accepted as the smoothest operating agency for dispensing social services in the nation, with the lowest administrative costs. Its assistance, in some form or another, reached one out of every three Oklahomans, the blind, the mentally ill, neglected juveniles, the old folks.

Lloyd Edwin Rader was the longest serving Director of Social Services in America and was one of the most respected persons in his field. He was considered in Washington to be the final authority in the delivery of social services. What worked, what didn't. And it had paid off for Oklahoma.

He had become a self-taught genius in taking over other under-financed state agencies, absorbing them into the department and funding them with sales tax funds plus a heavy infusion of federal dollars. Legislators loved it and him, because the general fund money thus freed could be used to raise teachers salaries or build projects back in the home district. In the 1950s and 1960s, Oklahoma politicians could boast there had never been a tax increase since the end of World War II.

Rader knew if he quit his legacy would be one of unparalleled public service in the face of great odds. His personal integrity and honesty were unblemished. His honors defied a complete listing. Some of them were:

Distinguished Service Award in 1969-1970, Oklahoma Association for Retarded Children; Award for Interest and Affairs of the Blind, 1970, Oklahoma Federation of the Blind; Award of Appreciation, 1973, United Cerebral Palsy Association of Oklahoma, Inc.; Citizen of the Year in 1975 for the Western Oklahoma Chapter of the National Association of Social Workers; Executive Directors Award, 1975; American Public Welfare Association; Distinguished Service Award, 1977, National Governor's Conference; Distinguished Service Award, 1977, Oklahoma State Medical Association; Distinguished Public Service Award, 1977, Oklahoma College of Osteopathic Medicine. He was a member of the Oklahoma Hall of Fame.

In the 27 years since he had laid his cowboy hat on the desk of Governor Murray and told him the job he offered was political suicide, he had served under eight governors – including two Republicans. So he decided that as soon as the 1978 gubernatorial election was over, he would walk over and talk with the newly elected chief executive about calling it quits. Before he had stayed on that old horse too long.

❖

Judge Luther Bohanon turned 76 that year. His work had just begun.

It became obvious that his plan for improving Oklahoma's prisons wasn't working the way he wanted it to. After four years of reform, prisons still were overcrowded. Health care services still were inadequate. Prisoners still were denied meaningful access to the courts.

Recreational facilities had been increased, drug abuse groups started, ethnic support groups, and a chapter of Alcoholics Anonymous permitted within the walls. Restrictions had been lifted on mail and reading material, a barber shop established in each cellblock, and new systems started to protect prisoners from physical abuse and to discourage loan sharking. But it just wasn't working the way Bohanon wanted it to work.

He had held hearings every six months to monitor the state's actions to obey his decree, and by 1977, those hearings had shown that conditions in the state's prisons had again reached a critical level. State Senator John Young of Sapulpa had studied the prisons and reported on their conditions in a letter to Governor David Boren, who was already in a campaign for the U.S. Senate. The letter was ignored. Young passed a bill authorizing an intensive state study of prison standards. Boren vetoed the law.

After a hearing in May of 1977, Judge Bohanon had issued his second order in the Battle case.

"Persons are sent to prison as punishment," he wrote, " not for punishment."

In Oklahoma prisons, he said, overcrowding and unsanitary conditions were the rule rather than the exception. He ordered the state to reduce the prison population at McAlester and at the State Reformatory at Granite at rapid rates. He said every prisoner housed in a cell must be provided at least 60 square feet of space or 75 square feet of space in a dormitory. When anti-prison-reform protestors screamed, Bohanon told them that their king-sized beds had more than 50 square feet of space.

On September 11, 1978, Bohanon issued his Battle III decision. In a scathing summation, he retraced the history of the case and of the defendants' failure to comply with his rulings.

He ordered wooden dormitories at the Lexington correctional facility closed within three months. The state legislature would, he said, appropriate money to replace deficient cell houses at Granite and McAlester within ten months or those facilities would be shut down. All deficient cell blocks were to be permanently closed no later than May 1, 1981. Construction of replacements had to begin within 14 months. He demanded obedience to his prior orders. Tight schedules were spelled out for compliance.

"My defendants are not in the legislature," protested Amy Hodgins, assistant attorney general, "and there is no way they can appropriate money."

Governor David Boren attacked the decision and directed Corrections Director Ned Benton and Attorney General Derryberry to appeal.

"For the state to simply sit back and give in to an order forcing the spending of $50 million of the taxpayers money is absolutely unthinkable," Boren said, "That will never happen as long as I am the governor of the state of Oklahoma."

Judge Bohanon underlined the words when he read of it in an *Oklahoma City Times* story, and noted mentally that Governor Boren, who was in a close runoff election for the Democratic nomination for the U.S. Senate, would be long gone from the governor's chair when the deadline arrived for appropriation of the funds.

Boren, in a debate with senatorial opponent Ed Edmondson, called for an end to lifetime appointments for federal judges such as Bohanon.

But there were those who saw the wisdom – or the inevitability – of the judge's words. Speaker of the Oklahoma House of Representatives Bill Willis and Oklahoma Senate President Pro Tempore Gene Howard said they felt that the legislature had no choice but to obey the order.

Corrections Director Benton, a reformer himself, politely told the governor that the decision whether to appeal rested not with the governor, but with him and the other named defendants in Battle's lawsuit.

In the spring of 1983, U.S. District Court Judge Luther Bohanon took a personal tour of "Big Mac," the maximum security prison at McAlester, oldest prison of the system that had kept him involved as overseer of Oklahoma Corrections for almost a decade. He nodded his head like a pleased parent on his tour through the cell blocks, the law library, kitchen and dining rooms, new construction sites, the trusty building and the prison meat packing plant.

"Surprised," he said. "Amazed. Delighted. Much better than I'd ever dreamed. They've got an excellent staff. The people are professionals. They know what they're doing."

Under his rulings, Oklahoma had spent hundreds of millions of dollars on construction of new institutions and renovation and expansion of existing ones, and Bohanon had been vilified as severely as he had for his orders integrating the schools of Oklahoma. But he had not yielded. And as a result, a prison system once described as one of the most inefficient, archaic and corrupt in the nation, ruled with unmerciful discipline and brutal guards, became the first major system in the United States to be fully accredited by the American Correctional Association.

Why the personal visit?

After all those years of sitting on the bench, studying and listening to other people's views of Oklahoma's prison, Bohanon said he just wanted to see what a revolution in corrections looked like up close.

In December of 1983, Judge Bohanon stepped out of the case, and a neutral judge ruled that Oklahoma had met its obligation to see that rights guaranteed under the U.S. Constitution were not left at the prison gate.

42

Death of a Branch of Government

"He was his own separate branch of government. He just simply dominated everybody. He let us control things that didn't matter in exchange for control over what did matter."

It was a cold, blowy day in early December of 1986, and Cleta Deatherage Mitchell was talking about Lloyd Rader, and she was talking about him because he was dead. Cleta was born the year before Lloyd Rader became director of Oklahoma welfare, and she went into politics and became the only woman in the history of Oklahoma to chair the powerful House Appropriations and Budget Committee. And thus, she came face to face with the Oklahoma political legend when he still got up every morning and went to work. She remembered one of her favorite stories.

A young couple in her Norman district had, they told her, been waiting a heart-breaking two years to adopt a child. They wanted one desperately, and they weren't getting anywhere. There seemed no reason for it and no way to get around the unfairness of it. Cleta looked the situation over and saw it was a hopeless thing. And this young woman at the cutting edge of new-age politics did what the Old Guard had done for years. She called Lloyd Rader. And when he called her back, he said, "Their baby is ready. Why don't you call them and tell them the good news."

"I can't tell you the feeling that you got when you could call people like that and tell them that things had been taken care of," Cleta was saying. "You tried not to get involved, but you couldn't help it. You asked for things, and Mr. Rader kept track of that. It was never spoken, but he had an amazing ability to establish the debt. He was a good man in so many ways. I only regret that he didn't retire four or five years earlier. Then his exit might have been more graceful."

He tried. He really did. Lloyd Rader tried to get out. Back in 1979 when George Nigh became governor. Mr. Rader had gone down to talk to Nigh, and his offer to resign was not routine. He had sworn to himself that he would not ride that old political horse until it threw him. But George Nigh had asked him to stay. Just a while. Fight one more fight. Build the state a model adult hospital to match the model Children's Hospital of which Oklahoma now was so proud.

"George," said Mr. Rader, "I probably am too old for that hard a fight."

But in the end, he had shrugged as he always had when governors asked him to try to do something that looked impossible.

"If you want to have an accredited medical school, dental school and other health schools, I guess you've got to have an accredited hospital for those programs."

Not long after that, the new provost for University Hospital came in from California, and they held a reception for him at the Petroleum Club in downtown Oklahoma City. Mr. Rader attended it, of course, and when he came back to his office, it was after five o'clock, but his staff still was working, as usual.

"The governor," Mr. Rader told them, "has just announced that we are going to take over the adult hospital."

"Well," said Vera, who could say such things and get away with it, "we got the kitten and now, we've got the old cat, too."

On March 24, 1980, Governor George Nigh signed House Bill 1713, transferring the failing University Hospital from its Board of Trustees to the Department of Human Services. The name was changed to Oklahoma Memorial Hospital, and Lloyd Rader set to work on a project that had defied the efforts of much younger men. And he did it.

He made old University Hospital into Oklahoma Memorial, and it joined Children's Hospital on the list of things of which Oklahoma could be proud. The two of them together became centerpiece for a third.

University of Oklahoma Health Sciences Center grew into a 180-acre complex that was among the top ten regional health centers in the nation. There were four public and two private hospitals, a number of private clinics – eye clinic, blood institute, allergy, dermatology – together with family clinics, emergency medicine clinics, a rehabilitation center and the like. Colleges of medicine, dentistry, nursing, allied health, public health, and graduate college. Numerous academic buildings and research buildings, a central library and a self-contained chilled water and heating plant.

The complex became one of those marvels few could believe came from Oklahoma. Economic boosters who wouldn't look at it when doctors were refusing to operate there began to point to it with pride. You never would have believed there was any difficulty in getting it built. Few know the story of how it came to be.

It started on a Sunday. Getting late. Gene was in Oklahoma City, getting ready for Monday's legislative session. The telephone rang. It was Mr. Rader. "Now, senator, you've got to help me here."

Usually, when the telephone rang in Gene's room on a Sunday afternoon, it was Mr. Rader, and whatever he was doing, Gene would quit and go see Mr. Rader. Often, Gene still would be there when the too-late Sunday turned into a too-early Monday.

"We have collected $100 million and some dollars from the federal government that Oklahoma really isn't entitled to," Mr. Rader had told him on that Sunday afternoon. "I've put it away at interest, but the secretary of Health Education and Welfare is going to demand that we reimburse him."

"What do you want me to do?"

"I think we can delay paying these fellows that money long enough to draw enough interest to do some good for Oklahoma. I want you to help me find a law firm that can handle it."

Gene shopped the nation and finally found a big law firm in the east. The two of them went up to see them and told them what Mr. Rader wanted to do. It was years before the U.S. Department of Health Education and Welfare finally got Oklahoma into court to answer for that $100 million. And it was the oddest thing. Once in court, Oklahoma shrugged and admitted it had no defense. The money had been paid to Oklahoma by provable mistake. Oklahoma still had the $100 million in a special account. Mr. Rader agreed to give it back. Nothing was said of the interest money it had been collecting. And that interest money on $100 million was the seed from which grew Oklahoma's medical center marvel. Got it started on its way. That was the way Lloyd Rader worked. It was years before Gene would tell the story.

"No one really knows that, I think, but me," he said. "That was Lloyd Rader at his finest."

So it was, Lloyd Rader worked his last miracle. And he never recovered from it.

In 1981, the Department spent $887 million in federal and state funds for programs that touched one of every three Oklahomans. But no matter how Mr. Rader turned and twisted and figured, it was obvious that – for the first time since he had taken the job – the department would have to ask for a $23 million appropriation from the state's general revenue fund to tide it through a cash flow problem which would be corrected before the following year. University Hospital – the old cat – caused it, Vera Alder said.

"The hospital was half finished when we got it. They had a building they couldn't finance and that they couldn't operate because they had nothing to use to operate it with, and by the time we got that paid for and straightened up, we were broke."

Actually, there were many reasons.

In Washington, Republican President Ronald Reagan was talking about limiting what any state could receive in federal welfare money. In Oklahoma, depression-trained lawmakers who knew what a little bit of eating money in their pocket meant to the needy were replaced by young, ambitious men and women who had never known anything but good times. Old-timers dubbed them polyester politicians, college-trained and ambitious to make a name for themselves. They felt no awe for Mr. Rader. Resented his power. Showered him with constant requests for information. Mr. Rader kept them at bay for a long time by drowning them in paper. Knowing that they would have to spend the long dark-to-dark hours that he spent at work in order to understand them. Knowing they didn't have the time or the willingness to do so.

University Hospital was originally planned to be done in six years, but Mr. Rader was induced to try to finish the job in three. And his ability to stretch and twist and multiply the state's two percent welfare sales tax to take on more and more of the state's obligations had been stretched to the breaking point.

"Governor Nigh kept on demanding this and that," Vera said. "A helicopter that could go to this part of the state or that part of the state and pick up critically ill people. Mr. Rader built a helicopter pad and everything. Governor Nigh wrote Mr. Rader a note how much he was pleased about having the helicopter. Said it was the proudest day of his life. But all those things stripped the department and it broke it."

The shield of invincibility had been pierced.

Lloyd Rader was 76 years old. He had been a farmer and a rancher and a businessman, and he had been good at all of them. He had run a construction company. He was an accountant, and he had gotten a degree in law after being named director of welfare to better prepare himself for the job. And he took all those talents, and, instead of becoming a millionaire CEO of a giant corporation, he turned all of his talents and all of his time to helping the people of Oklahoma who could not get help elsewhere. And he did it with a masterful hand.

This "Binger storekeeper who won't last a year" had turned the Oklahoma welfare department into a national celebrity of state institutions. And so, by any criteria, the year 1982 should have been a year in which the aging Rader was crowned in glory for the difference he had made in the lives of so many Oklahomans. But he wasn't.

Once that myth of invincibility had been pierced, the investigations started, as they had started with Donahue. As they always do. Almost daily television and press assaults started in February. They were followed by state and federal investigations that alleged everything. Juvenile abuse in the shelters Mr. Rader had created. Purchasing practices, the handling of nursing home inspections, improper use of consulting contracts. And everybody who knew, knew it was because Lloyd Rader had amassed too much power and used it too well for too long. Vera Alder always declined to admit that she actually set her dog on OSBI agents when they came to her home to interview her. But she did admit the dog had tried to bite them. They came, she said, to ask her if Lloyd Rader – who inventoried down to the staplers when he took over an agency – had used state money to built a new clinic for his doctor son.

In the early months of 1982, Lloyd Rader made a very different kind of trip to Washington, and he took Gene with him for a very different reason. Senator Arlen Specter, a Republican from

Pennsylvania, summoned Mr. Rader before his subcommittee on juvenile affairs for the Senate Judiciary Committee.

Gene remembers:

> Senator Specter started trashing Mr. Rader. On and on. We sat through the damnedest day of just sheer trashing and harassment. I got Mr. Rader aside.
>
> "Mr. Rader, we need to figure some way out of this. This guy will go on forever."
>
> "Well, what are we going to do?"
>
> "I happen to know Strom Thurmond. He is chairman of the Senate Judiciary Committee, and I think the chairman can take over any subcommittee and chair it anytime he wants to. If you feel comfortable doing it, we will go talk with him." Mr. Rader was, of course, delighted.

It was enough that Strom Thurmond was a United States senator and chairman of the powerful Judiciary Committee, but he was much more than that. Former public school coach, self-made attorney, former judge, a ranger with the United States 82nd Airborne who jumped into the battle at Normandy Beach on D-Day and earned five battle stars. During the war he won a total of 18 decorations and medals, including Merit with Oak Leaf Cluster, Purple Heart, Bronze Star for Valor, Belgian Order of the Crown, and French Croix de Guerre. He came home to become governor of South Carolina, and later to be the first U.S. senator ever elected by write-in votes. Senator Strom Thurmond knew the right of things. And when he spoke, people listened.

> He showed up the next morning and chaired the subcommittee and we were out of there by noon. The hearing was concluded. No one ever figured out why that hearing ended that way. That's why I always root for Strom

Thurmond. Everything he does, because I remember that. I don't care if he's old. He deserves to get re-elected as long as he wants to. I won't ever forget that. Mr. Rader never forgot it, either.

But the litigation went on and on and…

By mid-year of 1982, it became apparent that the investigations were too pervasive. The old horse just couldn't be ridden any more. Legislation was passed diverting the state's two percent sales tax from the hands of Mr. Rader and into the hands of the Legislature. The story was over.

When there was nothing more that he could do, Lloyd Rader looked at his accusers with those cold, blue-steel eyes that had never wavered.

"I am square with myself," he told them, "and with God Almighty."

And he had set about trying to help them find a qualified successor.

Oklahoma began disassembling the greatest state institution for public service in the United States. Mr. Rader did not have to watch for very long. For three years, he served as an advisor to Congress and the President of the United States and to St. Anthony Hospital.

And then he died.

Of pneumonia on Dec. 6, 1986, at Presbyterian Hospital in Oklahoma City. He was 80.

"One of Oklahoma's Giants," said Senator David Boren, who was ten years old when Mr. Rader took over the department. As governor, Boren used to ride his bicycle over to the Sequoyah building on weekends and take his children in to see Mr. Rader at work in his office.

So of all the years of Lloyd Rader's political life, the year that should have been the best was the worst. But the truth of it resides in history, and in the memories of the old-timers who were there and watched what changed in Oklahoma just because he was here.

Getting together in little groups, they put together things even they hadn't put all together before.

> He built all the capitol office buildings. In 1959, we established the Capitol Improvement Authority. Lloyd set that up to build the first two office buildings, which were Sequoyah and Will Rogers, issued bonds to be retired from the rent, then arranged for the state treasurer to buy the bonds. That kept us out of the dilemma of having to have a vote of the people on revenue bonds.
>
> That worked out so well, we built two more. The Mike Connors building for the Tax Commission, and the Oliver Hodge Education Building.
>
> We created a state construction force headed by a guy named Bill Sylvester. He is a state employee. All of his help are state employees. He's saved the state of Oklahoma millions and millions of dollars because he can move his crew in and do something a lot cheaper than you can contract it out.
>
> When we had the riots at the McAlester prison, he moved in and rebuilt it. Riot up at the Hominy Prison, he rebuilt that at half the cost of contracting it out. They rebuilt the state Senate chambers. They rehabbed the building where the Oklahoma School for Science and Math is. They work for all the agencies of government. Always a lot cheaper than you could contract it out. And it was Lloyd Rader's invention. Lloyd Rader had a great capacity for that kind of administration.

And they would pause and drop their heads and struggle with their own thoughts.

"Did we finally put too much on Lloyd?"

"Probably, probably. You know what a hard driver he was. He worked all the time. We probably did overtax him in his seventies. Had he remained strong and healthy..."

And they would raise their heads and try to justify it.

"But, he was sound in his thinking. I never did see Lloyd Rader when I thought his faculties were impaired by age or anything else. The press just developed him into some kind of a powerful ogre or something. He was not that. He was a powerful good guy."

And they would rub their hands together slowly and decline to look up at all. And when they did, there was something in them you will never hear them speak aloud. What they would say was:

"Don't ever say anything bad about Mr. Rader in front of me. I will hit you."

His family buried him in Little Rock, Arkansas, near where his only son lived. Beside his beloved Ruth. But they couldn't change his legacy. Lloyd Rader was an Oklahoman who loved Oklahoma.

Loved her least fortunate most of all.

Those are the things the people who really knew Lloyd Edwin Rader gathered to discuss on that cold, blowy day in December of 1986.

43

What Better Praise?

Somewhere off in the gloom, Hayden Donahue could hear an Oklahoma woman needing help. He stood for a moment, letting his eyes adjust. Slowly, it assembled before him. A large, dismal room packed full of helpless people. Bars on the window were so thick they shut out the bright, sunny day that was going on outside. Finally, he made out the woman crouched in the farthest corner of the room. So many beds were so close there was no way to her from where he was. He hoisted himself onto the bed and walked the length of the room, bed to bed, placing his feet so he did not step on the faces of any of the pitiful people looking up at him for help.

That's how it was. That is how he found it when he came home to Oklahoma many years ago. And because he came back, it is not that way anymore.

That's what everybody kept trying to say when they all gathered in September of 1991 to honor Dr. Hayden Hackney Donahue when he retired for the third and last time. This time as director of the Hayden Donahue Training Institute. He was nearing 80, health failing, eyesight failing, but the lopsided grin intact; the compassion and love still making their way out through the popbottle thickness of his glasses.

One of the giants, they said.

"Legendary founding father of Oklahoma's system of mental health care."

"More than anyone else, Dr. Hayden H. Donahue deserves credit for ending Oklahoma's shameful treatment of mental patients and building a modern system that has served as a worldwide model for care of the mentally ill," said the ultra-conservative *Daily Oklahoman* newspaper.

"Indomitable, tenacious, bullheaded, politicking genius," said the liberal *Oklahoma Observer.*

"A man whose life has been devoted to those who live in life's shadows," said State Senator Gene Stipe, his old friend from Peaceable Mountain.

But they still couldn't say it.

Chosen from among 35,000 psychiatrists for the Distinguished Service Award from the American Psychiatry Association for a lifetime of service, taking his place alongside Karl Menninger and Anna Freud.

A colleague, perhaps, came closest to saying it.

He was Dr. Charles Smith, one of the first psychiatric residents drawn to Oklahoma by Donahue's innovative program back in 1955.

"To watch Dr. Donahue walk down the halls of the ward" he said, "is to see love and compassion."

And because of that, hope now waits in rooms filled with bright, morning sunshine where despair lived in dark, dirty rooms.

Oklahoma, and the world, are not the way that they were when he came. What greater memorial could there be?

❖

Another gathering of a most unusual nature was held in that landmark year. It was thirty years after U.S. Senator Bob Kerr had brought the United States' legislative process to a halt to get Luther Bohanon appointed U.S. District Court Judge from Oklahoma. Almost 20 years from the day Bohanon saw himself hanging in effigy from the overpasses of Oklahoma City streets. Almost 20 years after his wife had answered the telephone and heard that voice:

"Your husband will be a dead man come Friday."

It was the annual Brotherhood/Sisterhood Banquet of the Oklahoma City region of the National Conference of Christians and Jews.

Luther Bohanon – whose name had been reviled from border to border in Oklahoma and across the nation by every kind of reactionary extremist nameable – was given the Humanitarian Award for exhibiting outstanding leadership. Folks finally could see it. Luther Lee Bohanon was honored for being the kind of man whose work made the world a better place to live.

The month before the banquet, 30 years after the case of the Oklahoma City optometrist's son being barred from Northeast High School was placed on his desk, the United States Supreme Court upheld Bohanon's ruling that the Oklahoma City School District finally was fair and equal. One district. One people. Students going to school where they wanted to go to school without regard to their race.

It still was a simple thing to Bohanon: "You either have the courage, or you don't."

Wade and his wife were sitting on the edge of the bed talking when the phone rang. She answered it, and her eyes got that scared look Wade had not seen in them for a long time. She covered the phone with one hand. Whispered.

"It's that old Ku Klux Klansman again."

She handed the phone to Wade. He had almost forgotten Imperial Wizard Johnny Lee Clary.

"Hello."

"Hello, brother."

Wade almost dropped the phone. It had always been "hello, nigger," before.

"What do you want, Mr. Clary?"

"Rev. Watts, the Lord has called me to preach."

"Doggone."

"Rev. Watts, I never could forget what you told me after that debate on the radio."

"What was that?"

"About how I could never do enough to you to make you hate me."

"Well, Mr. Clary, give me the privilege of letting you preach your first sermon in my church."

"Okay, Rev. Watts, where is your church?"

"You ought to know, Johnny, you burned it down."

44

Just Too Good To Be Political

On a beautiful first mid-morning of February in 1997, with the sun warming and the grass just starting to green, State Senator Gene Stipe – the longest-serving state legislator in the world at age 72 – pulled his car into the driveway of his home in McAlester. Got out. Walked over to the rolled-up copy of *The Daily Oklahoman* on the drive, snapped off the rubber band and opened it. Slumped.

"E.T. Dunlap died," he said.

"…of a stroke at Presbyterian Hospital in Oklahoma City. He was 82.

"Dunlap was chancellor of higher education from 1961 to 1982, a period during which enrollment soared. He oversaw the growth of junior colleges across the state."

When Elijah Thomas Dunlap had completed the jump from Eastern Oklahoma State College president to Chancellor of Higher Education for the State of Oklahoma in 1961 he hadn't even changed his pace. It took him 20 years, but he completed the dream he developed sitting in the ice-slick saddle of his horse in the mountains of Latimer County. And that dream was to bring the most education possible within reach of every child born in or brought to the State of Oklahoma. As chancellor, he did the same

Chancellor E.T. Dunlap

thing to higher education, except in reverse. As he had brought high school within reach of every country-bound elementary school graduate, he set out to bring college within reach of every city-bound graduate of high school.

Oklahoma was predominantly rural when its colleges were established, and that is where most of the colleges were. When farmers began migrating to the cities hunting work in the 1940s and 1950s, the rural colleges were no longer in the right places to meet the needs of kids who had been moved to the city. E.T. couldn't haul the grownup kids in shiny new school buses back to the rural colleges, so he set out to bring the colleges to the cities.

Just as he had used the slender staff of the fledgling Oklahoma Legislative Council to bring all the bits and pieces of common school law together into a code, he built his own research staff as chancellor and did the same thing for the colleges. He pushed through the legislature in 1965 a codification of all the laws that had ever been written in Oklahoma concerning higher education. And then he indulged his first love. E.T. launched a continuing study of Oklahoma Higher Education. Everything about it. From the first time men began to think about it until just the day before yesterday.

New, comprehensive, community colleges were needed desperately in the metropolitan areas of Oklahoma City and Tulsa where high school students were stranded just as surely as those farm kids were stranded in the backwoods. And, before E.T. was through, he was credited with building three new institutions with five campuses in Tulsa and Oklahoma City, serving more than 35,000 students each fall semester. He converted five local junior colleges to state colleges, creating a state junior college system where there had been a hodgepodge of small institutions, some local and some state-run. Those 14 colleges and two-year branches now enroll about 40 percent of all students and nearly 60 per cent of all freshmen in Oklahoma higher education. Forty-one institutions throughout the state have campuses or facilities that bear his name.

E.T. Dunlap revolutionized education in Oklahoma as Donahue revolutionized mental health and Lloyd Rader turned welfare into something nobody had ever seen. But, E.T. hadn't let them do to him what they did to Lloyd Rader.

He told them in 1982 that Oklahoma's higher education program was in good health and that he was going to go home while he still was. They asked him to stay, too. Just a little while. Fight one more fight. But, E.T. wasn't about to bite into that trap.

"It is a good time, in my judgement," he told them, "to stop."

And they gave him the keys to a new, $18,000 Cadillac Coupe de Ville, and kidded him for a while about his rambling conversations, and Elijah Thomas Dunlap went home to live as Chancellor Emeritus with all the admiration and respect he had earned in a lifetime dedicated to the people of the State of Oklahoma.

Standing in his driveway holding *The Daily Oklahoman* in his hand, Gene shook his head over the growing store of memories in his head.

"Those old boys were so good it didn't make any difference whether you were a Democrat or a Republican. Nobody dared fire them for some political appointment. E.T. Dunlap was one of those."

He folded the paper and put it under his arm.

"I've got to go to E.T.'s funeral."

The Rev. Wade Watts

45

That Stuff Jesus Said Do

Wade Watts died on December 15, 1998, a Tuesday. And on December 16, flags all across the State of Oklahoma were flown at half-staff in honor of the little black farm kid from Eufaula who didn't want to spend his life following a mule with the corn leaves cutting at his ears.

In the half-century that he tried to do that stuff Jesus talked about – "speaking kindly to you and all that stuff when you heaping fire on me" – he became a nationally known civil rights figure. He prayed before Congress, he was appointed to the U.S. Civil Rights Commission by President Lyndon B. Johnson, and he was honored in many ways large and small. But, there were two things in his life of which he was the proudest.

One was young John Clary and how trying to do that stuff Jesus talked about converted that old Ku Klux Klan fella.

The other was his family: thirteen children who got their educations without going through what he did and became doctors and nurses and housewives and laborers and just everyday folk in a different Oklahoma than the one in which he grew up.

46

An Uncommonly Common Man

J.I. Stipe died in early March of 1989 in McAlester's Regional Hospital, just across an expanse of trees and grass from the Carl Albert Regional Community Health Center, the green copper roof of which can be seen from the J.I. Stipe Community Center where younger old men still play dominoes and talk of how it was when the coal died. J.I. was 94. His black-haired boy the folks on Peaceable Mountain called Injin Joe was with him when he died.

"It is okay, son," J.I. told him. "I am just worn out."

Here is one of the memorials:

> J.I. Stipe's name will not be written into the history books as a doer of great deeds since he has not accomplished a task of historic consequence. But our nation was not conceived nor has it endured under the concept that a man must be a statesman to be of importance. The heritage of America is that men have the right to govern themselves and that free men have a responsibility to one another. J.I. Stipe

is representative of the uncommonly common man in America who believes in God and has fought for country, who believes in the strength and importance of the family unit, who recognizes there is no substitute for hard work and has faith in youth and future.

J.I. Stipe is what Woodrow Wilson referred to when he said, "The things that the flag stands for were created by the experience of a great people. Everything it stands for was written by their lives."

It would have embarrassed J.I. Stipe, but he would have liked it. His blackheaded boy liked it, too. Most of it. The part he couldn't quite accept was where it said his daddy's name would never be written into any history books. It just seemed to him that it should. He had seen in his daddy a quality he could not name – a kind of being a hero without knowing you were a hero at all – but Gene knew that quality when he saw it in other people, and it helped him throughout his life in choosing his friends. It was the same quality whether the man was a governor or a hoehand. Just depended on the job a man was given to do.

And there were all those whose names were and will be written into the history books, but not in exactly the way they would have been if the writers of history had sat with them in their dark hours and their triumphs great and small. As Gene had. And shared the unknown whys of what they did.

A Gathering of Heroes is a history book of its own particular kind. J.I.'s name is written into it in honor of all those uncommonly common men whose names you will never hear. Along with some whose names already are written into other books. But, not in the way they are written here. Those names are written here in this way in honor of J.I., who would have loved them all. As did his black-headed son.

And now you know why this chapter is out of place.

And what this book has been about.

INDEX